Sarah Nock

Ponderings on Parkinson's

An inside view of Parkinson's Disease

Illustrated by Hans Diebschlag

With a foreword by Professor Andrew Lees MD, FRCP

Ferry House Books
www.ferryhousebooks.co.uk

First published in Great Britain in 2007 by Ferry House Books

Text copyright © Sarah Nock 2007
Illustrations copyright © Hans Diebschlag 2007
Foreword copyright © Andrew Lees 2007

A Catalogue record for this book is available from the British Library
ISBN-13: 978-0-9557011-0-8

Printed for MRT by Cambrian in the UK - www.mrtresponse.com

The paper and board used in production are natural recyclable products made from
wood grown in sustainable forests and manufactured in accordance with the
environmental regulations of the country of origin.

Mixed Sources
Product group from well-managed
forests and recycled wood or fiber
www.fsc.org Cert no. TT-COC-2200
© 1996 Forest Stewardship Council

FSC

Ferry House Books
Ferry House
Copthorne Bank
Copthorne
Crawley
RH10 3JF

www.ferryhousebooks.co.uk

Contents

DERBYNIWYD/ RECEIVED	1 1 MAR 2008
CONWY	
GWYNEDD	
MÔN	
COD POST/POST CODE	LL5 1AS

List of Illustrations

Foreword

All doctors deal with narrative in their everyday practice and the art of medicine with its goals of accurate diagnosis and appropriate treatment depend on listening to patients' tales. The translation of narrative into the medical case history is a prerequisite for good clinical practice. Recognition of this process should not be denigrated as a retreat to a pretechnological age or as an outmoded antiscientific tradition but as a practical response to medicine's radical uncertainty. The medical case report focuses, narrows and minimises and attempts to order the messy and confusing detail of human experience. The ability of a doctor to listen and empathise has become even more important as we move more and more to a fragile mobile urban society bereft of the medicine of neighbours. The patient is the doctor's laboratory and while biomedicine moves closer to becoming a pure science in its laboratories, at the bedside it remains a patient centred interpretative practice. This skilled process is the essence of good clinical practice.

Nothing can prepare one for a neurological illness which worsens with time and will never get better. Sarah Nock's illuminating and at times amusing descriptions of what it is like to live with Parkinson's represents triumph over adversity and will provide comfort to many. Much of what I have learned about Parkinson's disease has come from patient pathographies and Sarah's ponderings are a fine example of the genre. I wish this slim monograph the success and readership its rich insights unquestionably deserve.

Andrew Lees
Professor of Neurology The National Hospital for Neurology
Queen Square London

Being squeezed by a Giant Hand
(page 13)

Introduction

A while back, I wrote a perfectly gratuitous letter to my specialist at the National Hospital for Neurology in London. Here is most of it:

Whenever I read something about Parkinson's, or hear a radio programme or watch a television one, I never feel any the wiser. I mean, I might feel more clued up about what is being done for us and other lovely things, but if I didn't have it myself I would be no nearer knowing how it actually felt. And I find no one seems to have any idea—until I tell them. I think a metaphor is the answer and I have had one from nearly the beginning: the Giant Hand. It is like being squeezed by a Giant Hand. Always, when I "flip" and am consigned to my armchair in extreme discomfort, I have this mental picture of King Kong with that girl in his hand. Nothing shows of her but her extremities, which are helpless, useless; it is difficult to breathe, impossible to think, the only reality is the immediacy of the squeeze.

I've asked other people with PD if this is how they feel and they agree. I wonder if this would be general? I'm sorry to trouble such a very busy man with this, but I think it would help us all if our properly dopamined peers had some idea. You liked me saying I turned into a pumpkin when my medication ran out in the early days (Oh, happy days when that was all. Not even a valid metaphor as that was the fate of Cinderella's carriage). I might just mention that when I flip, my head turns into a colander (full of little holes); all my stored information and plans and intentions trickle out and thus I am quite literally empty headed when I recover. I then have to pick up all the pieces and cram them back in. Unfortunately, it is not long before the process is repeated. (I'm sorry I shall be leaving you such a porous object.)

(I must just explain that parenthesis about the porous object: I had promised my brain to research, to this hospital, on my death.)

I was glad to get that off my chest; it was frustrating that no one seemed to have any idea of what Parkinson's felt like, not even the doctors in the large teaching hospital where I volunteered for a couple of brain scans and having electric shocks to my head — no, certainly not them. Then, when I had forgotten all about it --- to my surprise, I had a lovely letter back. Professor Lees said he found my letter helpful, that he himself found it difficult to comprehend the nature of the condition as experienced by his patients; he needed to hear it from the horse's mouth. And, as the

14

ancient Romans knew, metaphors are the simplest way to get your message across. Professor Lees encouraged me to write more, and then to get my patient's insights published. What more could one want! With glee (and some difficulty, mostly after midnight) I wrote the following. And the first problem I wanted to explore was one that had perturbed me for some time: How to reassure your family and friends - and yourself - that you are not losing your marbles. Tricky (I speak for myself) but not impossible.

Sarah Nock
Summer 2007

*My head turns into a colander
(page 14)*

Chapter One

So What Do *You* Think You've Got?

I truly believe, sadly enough, that the first thing a person thinks, on being diagnosed with Parkinson's, is "I'll lose my mind!" This in spite of the evidence of the formidable intellect of the late Pope John Paul II, amongst others, that contradicts such an unwelcome thought. (It wasn't quite my first, that was "Thank God it is not Motor Neurone.") I'd been pretty sure of my condition, during the four months that I waited to see a neurologist, and when the kindly Registrar said, probably disliking being the bringer of bad news, "What do you think you have got?" I replied "The Shaking Palsy".

He looked at me a little oddly and manifested no knowledge of this ancient illness, possibly just determined to make me admit to something more explicit.

"It's mentioned in the Bible," I said. Actually, we cannot be entirely sure that it is the modern Parkinson's to which "Palsy" refers, but it seems likely. And if so it occurs five times, according to a brilliant friend who appears to know the whole Bible off by heart. It is mentioned in three of the Gospels, only John omitting it. I was fascinated by the historic nature of this illness, though made rather uncomfortable by the cure. In the one version, which I remember from my schooldays, Jesus forgave the man his sins, and he, who had been carried in on a litter, immediately walked away, a new man (or at least a pre-palsy one). This introduced a psychological aspect that one would rather not have to worry about. Almost as bad as having an illness that as yet does not have a name; and we know how the rest of the world would react to that: no name, no illness.

Eventually I muttered "Parkinson's" to the kind doctor and we took it from there. Incidentally, a tendency to digress would soon start to get me into trouble now. And should be avoided, unless you want some fun. But more of that anon.

I'd just like to say that I think that was the moment,

when one is first given a firm diagnosis, that one should be presented with a sheet of paper. And on this paper would be a little run-down of what Parkinson's actually is; the names of some books and articles that would be useful, to read or dip into; and a clarifying affirmation that our problem is to do with motor instructions and doesn't at all involve the thinking part of the brain Maybe they do do that now, but they didn't when I was first given this new modus vivendi, thirteen years ago - at the best place one could possibly be, a centre of excellence, the National Hospital for Neurological Diseases.

It was all right for me actually. I have a huge extended family including several doctors and other health practitioners; I got plenty to read and lots of sound and encouraging talk. But I know that not everyone is so lucky and all too often PD is hugged to the new recipient as a guilty and unpleasant secret.

But, to get back to the beginning, at the first opportunity I asked Professor Lees what the enhanced chances of Alzheimer's, or senility and that lot generally, were. He was reassuring and said very little more chance than if we did not have PD. But can these states be wished upon us and statistics thus altered? Depression can do it, can't it?

If we think we are going to lose our marbles, are we not more likely to? And how much more if our nearest and dearest think so too, quite openly? All you have to do to a person to destroy them is to chip away steadily at their self-confidence. And this can be done with the best, if unimaginative, intentions.

I know of one wife who dashed headlong to get Power of Attorney the very day her husband was diagnosed. She knew nothing whatsoever about PD and was determined not to find out; he was a write-off! I met him several times and we swapped symptoms, that delicious hobby which can be enjoyed by all sharing a particular malady. His were very similar to mine, but not so his family: whereas Peter - my darling husband, who died some eight years after my diagnosis - cuddled and stroked me when evil dreams caused me to moan or cry out, this wife banished her man to the far end of the house where his darksome misfortunes could not disturb her. And very soon he was in an old people's home, at sixty, while she went off on luxury cruises. There has to be more in it than this, doesn't there? Perhaps he had outraged her earlier by affairs or flirtations, or failure to adore sufficiently. I'm sure Aesop would have a fable for it: beware of causing resentment in those who will eventually have power and jurisdiction over you....

Chapter Two

Moment of Truth

It took me quite a long time and a quantity of conversational adventures before I cottoned on. An early example went thus: I was upstairs getting dressed. At that stage of the game, being on a trial drug (or a placebo) it was a very slow process, taking about an hour. And that day we were having a new gas cooker, a green one (turned out to be its only virtue), delivered, so when the dog barked noisily downstairs I knew what must be happening. But since my husband was down there there was no need to hurry, I thought.

When I eventually descended I found to my dismay, not the piece of equipment I had expected but a dear friend I had not. With her little grand-daughter.

"I'm so sorry, I thought you were a gas cooker"
(page 23)

"I'm so sorry, dear", I cried, "I thought you were a gas cooker!"

Then I turned to talk to the child.

Peter told me afterwards that her face had been a picture of dismay. With hindsight I came to realise that she really did think I had confused her with a gas oven. Now she would never have done that in the days before PD, so there we go. Foolishly, I forgot to mention it to her again, not until years later when she insisted: "But you used to hallucinate, Sarah, I remember it so well!"

Perhaps that was when I began to be a little bit more observant; people's attitudes towards me were subtly different, I noticed, more anxious; embarrassment could creep into a conversation in a way it never had before. Shortly after the last incident, another friend was driving me back from a lunch party.

"Have you seen Jo's adorable baby parrot?" I asked her.

There was no response; she stared sternly at the empty road ahead with an expression of great concentration. I just have to explain about Jo's adorable baby parrot: our hostess had a whole lot of these exotic birds and they actually bred in captivity, but one babe had been completely plucked by his mother at the age of a few months. Perhaps she didn't want him to leave the nest? Anyway, he couldn't, he had nothing at all to fly with, he was a naked, oven-ready baby parrot. Jo had taken him into her own hands and nursed him till he was in flyable plumage again, but it was the eyes! I have never seen such wise, benevolent and loving eyes in any bird; scarce in any human either. "I loved him to bits," admitted his second mother, "I could hardly bear to see him fly away." Looking at him tugged my heart strings too, so I tried again, in a louder voice:

"Have you seen Jo's adorable baby parrot?" My friend gasped with relief and one hand was slapped to her chest.

"Thank goodness!" she exclaimed, "I thought you said 'carrot'!"

So when I had enquired after her sighting of this loveable vegetable it hadn't elicited any response from her? Nothing on the lines of "What are you talking about, you silly old bag?" No, not that; she was not one of my oldest friends, but she might have said "I'm sorry, Sarah, I don't quite understand what you said just now?" But silence. Odd!

It is obvious I had still not got the message.

At that time I was working in London two days a week, thanks to the generosity of the word processor that was busy replacing the old typewriter wherever one went. The long, personal letters which I wrote for my boss, to her clients, ended up the first time round as one baffling word, dotted with extraneous z's, q's and p's. We tried fitting an Indian toe-ring to my thumb (friends were very enterprising) and it came down with a clatter upon the space bar, occasionally causing it to activate, but very soon we preferred the peaceful way of dissection after completion. What a wonderful invention was the WP; it enabled me to do a fascinating job that otherwise would have been quite impossible.

So there I was at this lovely job in the unspoilt environs of Marylebone. Mostly writing to troubled clients ("tell him to pull himself together", "encourage her; she's got more going for her than she thinks", "if I get another young woman who's done an assertiveness training course...!", "Find out what she thinks makes her too good for anyone else". These were some of the instructions scribbled on incoming correspondence, to give me guidelines). And every afternoon my incredible boss made me rest, wrapped in a duvet on the sofa of her lovely drawing room. A little snooze, so snug, so renovating; I saved all the most difficult letters for the sector after that.

Occasionally I had other duties, like entertaining an aged nun, showing her the high life. We must have looked quaint: she diminutive and ninety plus, hanging on and trying to keep me on the straight and narrow as I shook and wavered around. We made it to a well-known cake shop and had an enormous coffee éclair each, before deciding we'd "done" London, and tottering home again.

But what I eventually arrived at, was a moment of truth. One day, Boss and husband were waiting for me to gather my belongings and leave the office so they could lock up, but I had mislaid my keys. Then to my relief, something jangled on one hip:

"What's it got in its pocketses then?" I snarled.

A sort of cross between a snarl and a menacing whine.

There was a total silence, one that somehow vibrated. I looked up at them by the door, both of them were gazing straight ahead with expressions of dismay and apprehension.

"Haven't you read "The Lord of the Rings"? I demanded.

They shook their heads dumbly.

So thus they were introduced to a slimy little creature called Gollum, and I was introduced to a Golden Rule. And that Golden Rule is: Always Follow Through. Never let anyone escape without ascertaining that they know why you have said what you just said. And that there is no cause for alarm. Even if they do think it's a pathetic joke, they have got to realise it is legitimate. They should be reassured that you haven't actually lost your marbles.

A parrot on a carrot
(page 24)

Parkinson's
National Trust Chair
AD 2007

My mother's National Trust walking seat...total bliss
(page 30)

Chapter Three

On Not Looking Drunk On Victoria Station

I delighted in my part-time job. The journey up to central London was a trifle hazardous: these were still fairly early days, two to seven years after I was diagnosed (though Professor Lees said I had probably had PD for ten years already; I could go along with that) and the medication didn't quite match up to the symptoms. I was getting dystonia in my right foot a lot those days and when the piercing and unexpected pain shot into my foot, making it feel as though it were bent double in a kind of cosmic cramp, then I had to sit down immediately, but immediately.

I had this vision of crossing the great concourse at Victoria Station and sinking to the ground for want of a chair, while all the other busy clients of British Rail stepped over me, faces averted, because they were convinced I was drunk. That was when I brought out my mother's National Trust walking seat (not sure what they are officially called). We have never been parted since.

When folded its four feet become two and walk together with me in perfect harmony, a huge improvement on an ordinary stick. It is total bliss for letting you sit down whenever, wherever, at a moment's notice, at the light twitch of a thumb. I have sat on it waiting for lights to change so I can cross the road; I have sat on it in crowded trains; at cocktail parties (it does not deposit you down so low as a sofa, making it much easier to converse normally).

You make friends wherever you go: they all want to know where your amazing stick came from, how they can get one for themselves or spouse. (Particularly I remember sitting on it and knitting at a bus stop. Innumerable old women -- like myself -- came and told me nostalgically of their knitting days; days when knitting mattered.) Why, I wonder, does one see so few of these mobility marvels around?

Another little Parkinson's quirk was manifesting itself at that time. I do not know if it is a well known one; it is rather embarrassing. So as not to delay when buying things in shops I kept some money loose in my pocket to avoid scrabbling in my bag—I would put my hand in the pocket, and then be unable to get it out again! Not with any money in its grasp anyhow. A queue of disbelieving, irritated customers formed behind me.

It has to be admitted that we can look rather odd. Just in those times when the medication seems to have deserted us. The knees bend, refusing to straighten; the stomach juts out while the bottom does the same on the reverse, leaving a determinedly caved in back above. The forearms come up, dangling the hands submissively; I noticed that for years, seeing it in photographs, and, totally ignorant of the fact that this was a feature of Parkinson's, presumed I must have had a rabbit in my ancestry (it was rather disappointing to have such an interesting notion blown away). The shoulders hunch forward as if defending the chest and, indeed, that is being assailed by the Giant Hand, and breathing is difficult as a consequence; and the chin locks firmly on to the collar bone, making it impossible to look people in the face. Visualising all this, one can see what is happening: the powers-that-be are trying to turn us into space-saving balls. And apparently the central nervous system is responsible for this, turning us all inwards.

Now there are various things that can be done about this, and one of them I regard as a veritable silver lining to the cloud: women should not wear trousers. Hurray! It is one of life's great mysteries to me: why do women wear trousers, ever? I suppose it is not too bad if you are very young and very slim (but you would still look lovelier in a skirt); when you are old and sag, and Parkinson's gives a tweak to the inevitable sagging, it is grim. Skirts disguise this quite well, and, besides, skirts can be put on over your head, a vast improvement to hovering on one leg while you drag yourself into trousers. A great-aunt of mine once famously said that she thought she was beginning to be past her best, or her Sell By date, when she found herself trying to put knickers on over her head. To any male fellow Parkinsonians reading this, I apologise for gloating and recommend a kilt.

Obsessively, I must just finish my tirade against trousers. We have taken so much from men this century; we are tending to render them less than essential in every sphere. Do we really have to steal their clothes as well? And next time you are stuck in a traffic jam on the motorway and forced to spend a penny behind an inadequate bush, ponder on this apparel and its dire shortcomings.

Now what I was steaming up to say was that if we

look somewhat odd, we will of course be presumed to be odd. Mentally as well as physically. And that must not happen because once other people are convinced of your mental lapse, you will begin to think that way too - and, farewell, the thin red boundary is crossed. I believe that the physiotherapy, and the resultant exercises, that you will probably be offered by your GP, is very helpful.

I have not tried this, but over the years I have had regular acupuncture, say every three weeks, and cranial osteopathy, every two months or every one month if I am bad. And as I intend to explain later, I find them both absolutely marvellous. I can spring back into a more or less normal posture after a spherical period.

Complementary medicine will not do anything for Parkinson's per se, but I have found it to help mightily with symptoms, side effects and general deterioration.

Some of the little dragons have flat, square faces
(page 41)

Chapter Four

Here Be Dragons

Here be dragons indeed, hordes of them. The ancient mariners who put these stark three words on their maps, regarded the dragons, those unknown dangers to come, with a great deal of respect. As one dragon is worsted, or rendered less effectual for the time being, others smoke and bellow and can look very menacing. One is called narcolepsy, or if not the real McCoy, something very like that. Or in my case it can be something more dreadful, something to stun a dinner party into shocked silence. Unlikely to happen to anyone but me unless they also have a much loved sister living in Cornwall who happens to be the Mrs. Malaprop of the Modern Age. "Poor Sarah", she sighed, before electrifying her audience, "now she is suffering from Necrophilia."

In case you don't believe anyone could make that sort of mistake, I promise we have a bookful of them; and she once warned me against trusting a certain man because he was "trying to feather his own ends." Another time she famously had a fricassee on the telephone with her mother-in-law. Plenty more. And I can't resist that dinner party special: "Candlelight is a woman's provocative". We love her to bits, and not just because she has enhanced our language.

Despite being shunned by half the population of Cornwall, I resolutely maintain that it is narcolepsy that causes me to fall down the rabbit hole so often. Falling down the rabbit hole is code, or metaphor, in my family for falling asleep, that delicious sensation of drifting gently downwards while everything about you becomes "curiouser and curiouser", as happened to Alice before she reached Wonderland. That is when, so fascinated by the mysteries of one's new environment, that one tends to make totally inappropriate remarks, that reverberate amongst whoever happens to be there, probably kind people who have come to visit you.

Once I said, loudly and clearly: "I'm holding tight to my broom!" Could have had me burnt at the stake not all that long ago. And as I repeat it now I can still feel the whoosh of the cold night air and see the green eyes of my little black cat sparkle.

One of these random remarks as I fell suddenly into a deep and dream-filled sleep, has proved strangely useful. This dream was to the effect that my left leg was called Lionel and had been invited to a dinner party. Eventually my right leg was christened Laetitia. After that, whenever I was in a bad way and being helped to navigate the house by a family member, usually my son William, who walked backwards to our destination, "Lionel…Laetitia" would be intoned, "Lionel…Laetitia…", and somehow my feet, which had been taking tiny little shuffling and exhausting steps, would be encouraged into larger and more dignified paces. I recommend it.

Just to finish off this particular story, on another occasion I reportedly said: "What are my legs called?"

"Lionel and Laetitia," replied William.

"I know that." I said a little impatiently, "but what are their real names?"

I can't tell you how many weird and baffling statements I have come up with from the rabbit hole, but William's reaction is always the same: "Are you talking gobbledygook again, mother?" he says unconcernedly. "Yes, I guess I am," I say as the room around me resumes its familiar aspect. But others are not so fortunate as I am.

Before I joined that particular club we had a family friend who was forever dropping off; tea, coffee, cigarettes all being spilt in the process. His wife came into the room during one of his dream sequences. "Look out!" he called to her, "there's been a train crash! Bodies everywhere! Got to get them out! Get help!" When my husband and I called to visit Peter's old friend that evening and prepared to chat to him, we were told "Don't waste your time. His mind's gone. He won't understand a word you're saying."

There must have been a touch of disaffection in that family, too, and, poor man, told confidently and frequently that he had 'lost it', from now on reality was as hard to grasp as the crushed bodies that had so briefly surrounded him. Anyone can fall down the rabbit hole at times, and very pleasant it is too, usually. How I bless William for the 'gobbledygook' that clearly defines a small aberration, and is no indication of my real state. Just as necrophilia is not.

I was telling a friend about the "dropping off to sleep followed by inappropriate comments", and her eyes brimmed. "I can't bear it!" she murmured. She had

*Falling down the rabbit hole
(page 36)*

had a very dear uncle who had illuminated her childhood in South Africa; in later life he had developed Parkinson's and it was not long before there was a general consensus that he had lost his marbles. "But I see now," she said, "that it was all based on those after-nap oddities. Poor darling! He must have felt so abandoned." Thus we see that we have to save our friends and family from themselves; they must not be allowed to feel guilt and sorrow later. "There will be a certain amount of gobbledygook," you must say, "but it will not impinge on the real me. I shall be as wise and profound as ever, and will be happy to give you advice on life's little tribulations as and when requested."

On that pompous note (a joke, here I go again!) I could finish with the dragons, but there is the distant sound of huffing and puffing from those remaining, not such large and imposing specimens as before, but nasty, insidious and sly beasts. There is one I particularly dislike, but he shall be *nameless* (clue: right number of letters there) because I do not wish to be contaminated by him; I am ashamed when he sidles up behind me. It is like playing Grandmother's Footsteps: I keep whirling round and glaring--and yet he keeps coming that little bit closer.

(Perhaps it would be useful here to start the ball

rolling, or the marbles rolling, with an anagram: *pest I fly* from you!)

And here is one of many useful antidotes: "Bless our medical profession. The things they prescribe for us work magic!" Some people asked me once what it was like to have Parkinson's?

"Well," I said, "it is not too bad nowadays, because the medication is so good. But it must have been grim in the old days, when there was nothing to help." And then I added: "Especially if you didn't have good friends who would cut a hole in the roof for you."

There was a frozen, embarrassed silence. I should, of course, have explained that I was referring to that bit in the New Testament again, where the friends lower the man with the shaking palsy, on his litter, right at the feet of Jesus; the crowds pressing on him from all sides. But I felt too pi, too glib. It was just that we had such an interesting Scripture teacher at school: the only one, really, who made me lift my eyes from the book beneath my desk. And so another rumour was born. An own goal.

Some of the little dragons have flat, square faces, a grey, shadowy colour with insidious magnetic qualities. They almost suck people into their orbit;

they are not to be trusted. They work on the same principle as soma in "Brave New World"; they absorb, drug, destroy. Dehumanise. Just think of certain "Homes" where old people are stuck in their chairs, gaping uncomprehendingly at the television screen in their midst. We have to contribute a lot of our own effort, I think, to keeping our brains in pristine condition, and radio is a much trustier ally than television.

Yes, yes, of course I know, that sometimes it is inevitable that we will succumb, through no fault of our own, to Alzheimer's or senility. But meanwhile, let's hone what we have. I adore to be read to, and grandchildren and younger members of your family, or general well-wishers wondering what on earth to talk about, can help. And be educated themselves in the process whilst thinking they are merely doing a good deed. What is so lovely is that you can stop and discuss things en route through the book or article. Chess, Bridge and the cryptic crossword (my favourite and apparently extra useful because it encourages lateral thinking), are said to be very good for you.

When I feel particularly gruesome or acutely uncomfortable, so that I cannot do anything for myself, then I dearly like to be read poetry. There is the problem that the poem might be one I do not care for, so I have just assembled an anthology of my own. Now anyone can pick it up and read and I shall not be gritting my teeth. And such a fun project, too. Projects are the name of the game.

Lastly, a little anecdote, a very recent one that occurred just the other day. A lot of knowledgeable, and especially medical, people seem unable to comprehend that Parkinson's is perceived by the public as a mindblower. Well, I had to call out the Dyna-rod people after building rubble blocked our drains. I went out to meet the young man when I heard him come, taking my trusty stick/stool with me, as I always do outside the house.

"Do you have difficulty getting around?" he queried, eyeing this. "I do rather," I said. "I have Parkinson's, you see." This was riveting news! "Ah", he exclaimed happily, "that's the one where your brain rots, isn't it?"

"I'm holding tight to my broom!"
(page 36)

Chapter Five

How Is It For You?

I've been thinking a lot about Parkinson's recently, which isn't surprising when you've had this mischievous and intriguing malady as long as I have. I have just realised that I have had it for almost a third of my life. Leastways, as one of Alice's chums would say (more anon), I was diagnosed thirteen years ago, but Professor Lees told me at the time that I had probably had it for a good ten before that—which brings us to twenty three, and me to seventy. QED. Poor Peter; two thirds of my life were spent in my husband's company and blissful years they were too, but for quite a section of them (he died four years ago so I can't work out a neat proportion now) I must have been Parkinsonian. He didn't seem to mind. Perhaps he found it peaceful.

Looking back I am amazed how unquestioningly I accepted my slowing down. I drove down to Cornwall, in about 1990, to visit my sister; a long journey for me solo, but I spent a halfway night with friends in Dorset and kept off the motorways so that every hour I could have a little nap; a most imperative nap it was. And when one of the boys brought home a girlfriend who cooked a three course dinner for eight while I chopped a pepper, I comforted myself with the thought 'well, she is a professional'.

Photographs of me holding my hands up in front of me, hanging down as it were, in a somewhat helpless and beseeching manner, just brought out the usual family joke about a rabbit lurking in our background (Harvey, no doubt). I got a lot done because actually I think I must be quite efficient and good at short cuts and delegating, and three-weekly bouts of acupuncture kept me in some kind of remission, except for the dreadful migraines that got more and more frequent. And they were just the result of pushing myself against my fatigue and my unreasonable, so it seemed, lack of energy.

Like magic they dissolved when I started taking Levadopa.

The strange way of holding one's hands...
(page 48)

The strange way of holding one's hands, dangling from the wrist, is just one of the many clues to confirming Parkinson's. And this cannot be determined by blood tests or anything of that ilk, just by symptomatic behaviour. When you know these peculiarities well you can get quite good at spotting another member for the club. Shuffling foot steps; an apparent stiffness of the neck so that the body turns, rather than just the head, when its owner is in converse. Parkinson's people do not swing their arms when walking, a very convincing and helpful one that; their hands hang straight by their sides or are stuffed into pockets, or each other.

The face takes on a drooping lack of expression (everything hangs down as muscle power wanes and gravity takes over; I often have to give my stomach a helping hand on these occasions). The eyes stare a bit because they do not blink so often; it's a real struggle to smile and of course somehow you forget to swallow, so beware your first response when you have not spoken for a while; it can be a soggy one. Dribbling, I find, isn't too bad except in sleep. Anyway, that's not one of the really early symptoms.

There are all sorts of clever things involving the fingers that the neurologists use to ascertain your suitability for the club, and as far as I remember the only other clue for the layman is the sticking foot: one or other of them will every so often get glued to the floor, making a real mess of forward progression. A horrid one, this, as it makes it even more likely to fall over; I have found, oddly enough, that it helps to walk sideways, crossing one foot over the other, but someone must be holding your hands or you certainly will end up in a heap. However, it does help with unlocking, as it were. More on this stratagem later.

I was surprised to find that shaking is not an obligatory part of Parkinson's, more an optional extra. The three invariable attributes are imbalance (if you don't admit to having Parkinson's, they'll think you drink too much), slowness of movement (bradykinesia) and rigidity (much the worst). And if anyone says to you: "Relax!" you are likely to hit them. The two worst things anyone can say to me are "Relax!" or "Hurry up!" It's like "Hold your stomach in!" when you are pregnant; so impossible it's claustrophobic. By and large you are now going to remember all those dreams you've ever had, of creeping along slowly like a snail, or legs immured in mud, while something unspeakable comes up behind you, closer, faster....

But, you know, when someone says "What's your

problem?" - my trusty stick/stool as usual a good conversation opener - I notice that I reply "Parkinson's" with a small note of pride in my voice! Why can that be? It's a nice sturdy title with a slight cerebral ring about it...and now I remember something else. In my very early days I was at some function to do with the PD Society, release of a video I think it was, and speaking to some pleasant officer of that organisation who said "Do you know, we find Parkinson's affects more the intellectual part of our population." I have no idea whether that is a genuine statistic, but it was a lovely little boost. And I have told it to many new boys, with very pleasing results; a little more confidence to the drooping shoulders. Aren't we funny?

So, pride in Parkinson's? Well, there are some pros (as opposed to cons) if you are prepared to be a sleeves-rolled-up Pollyanna. So there we are, with a nice dignified name, though I'd like to forget about the Disease, sounds scary for other people; 'Syndrome' would be rather suitable, I feel. The manifestations are not all that grand, I know—but they are preferable to some others that are around: huge boils, permanent nausea and vomiting, endless migraines; Leprosy, Bubonic Plague and more nasties than I like to recount. There is a priceless clause written into our Parkinson's, is there not? A daily period of remissions (if the medication is right, and a few other things).

I have a friend, a young man who, when he quit the RAF and was getting organised for civil aviation, used to fly for my husband's ferrying company. Everything physical was on his agenda, mountaineering, skiing, tennis, you name it. He was taking a year off from flying a Middle Eastern king around to sail his sloop round the world - when he had a motorbike accident. Twenty-five years later and nothing has changed, he cannot do anything for himself (except use his brains mightily) and needs constant twenty-four hour care. What would he give, I think, for my chance to leap round the house and put a few things to rights, waddle (perhaps more appropriate than 'leap') into the garden for a bunch of flowers; pop round the corner for a beer at the pub? And as far as I can see this goes on for us for some time, diminishing, of course, and the wheelchair awaits, but plenty of time to prepare for that event. I almost feel guilty when, carefree as Cinderella before midnight, I whisk around trying to do all the little things I've been yearning to do—and thinking of my role model, immobile.

Yes, I am quite happy to admit to having Parkinson's. Let alone that if you don't they will think much worse things, just starting with the drink problem. It is a good opportunity to expand Parkinson's Awareness, as the Society does with its Week. And people are always so interested. "Really! And what is that like? What happens? Do tell." Only very rarely, with a long face: "Ah, my poor old Dad died of that." You don't really die of it; death is just aided and abetted, as it is by over-eating or smoking or all manner of rather more comforting and enjoyable things.

There don't seem to be any nicknames for People with Parkinson's, though in the film "Awakenings", where people with sleeping sickness (encephalitis lethargica) were given L-dopa, we are referred to as "Parkies"; rather affectionate I thought it sounded. Our medication had only just been initiated then, about fifty years ago; that was a fantastic breakthrough and it must have been a lot nastier 'ere then. That's another thing about Parkinson's for our grudging admiration: the best and most intelligent brains from all the civilised countries of the globe have been trained upon this eccentric and complicated condition - and I don't think they feel they are very much nearer yet to understanding why, or, indeed, wherefore. Perhaps there'll be another breakthrough soon, for people nowadays there is always a lot of hope available, Personally, I'm not counting on it: there's habitually something amazing being researched and it will be on the market in five years time, but before five years is up that has been long forgotten and abandoned.

And that, incidentally, is one of the times the media, unaware but carelessly, manages to confuse the public. "Big breakthrough!" it cries, "in stem cell research. Will be very valuable to sufferers from Alzheimer's and Parkinson's." I do think that it is this oft repeated pairing that programmes the public, including very many Parkinson's people themselves, into thinking the two conditions are similar. Yes, I know they are both seated in the brain but there the connection ends. My heart goes out to those who have Alzheimer's, it is extraordinarily sad, but we should be doing everything possible not to fall into that particular trap unnecessarily—and that means positive thinking.

I always thought that one of the best things one learned in school, terror at the time, was the Debate. Being given a motion to defend that one did not believe in was marvellously enlarging. Hence I will continue dragging the shallows for the defence of Parkinson's. A historical illness, too! Not only those five mentions in the Bible (although we cannot perhaps be certain that the palsy was definitely PD) but elsewhere in literature. I sometimes wonder whether Medusa had a hand in it, too? She was the loathsome creature in the Greek myths whose hair was live and slimy snakes wriggling out of her scalp, above a most ferocious glare. Anyone who looked upon her countenance was turned to stone.

Where did that idea come from? I call being "off" or "flipped", or whatever else it is known as, the Medusa Effect; one is almost literally turned to stone; head always slightly on one side, motionless and in the grip of the Giant Hand. Not nice. Perseus eventually slew Medusa and, sticking her decapitated head on to the front of his shield, went off to rescue Andromeda from the sea serpent, which didn't stand a chance because it looked at Perseus' shield, and with a great thrashing of coils sank leadenly into the depths of the sea. But could that story have grown up around the bizarre tribulations of PD?

The Medusa Effect
(page 53)

Chapter Six

Bizarre Tribulations

The bizarre tribulations of Parkinson's, that's what I was heading for, though a stream of consciousness delayed arrival. You have the three main problems: instability, slowness (the food is always cold before it reaches the mouth) and rigidity. But there are a mass of little, idiosyncratic non-functions or what have you, which are very intriguing. All the ones I have, I have found at least one other person to have also, but I expect there are many more and I'd love to know how they manifest.

A very major, to me, malfunction I refer to as "The Princess and the Pea", and I think it may come under the category of "Not a lot of people know that" because nobody ever seems to when I tell them. I'm

"The Princess and the Pea"

(page 57)

being a little discursive perhaps, but before I explain I'd just like to comment on children's stories, because quite a few of them flash by, providing the metaphors for this extraordinary condition.

I absolutely love children's books, the ones that have survived the test of time, and some latter-day ones that I hope will do the same. I do read grown-up books as well, quite a lot in fact, but I have never felt it necessary to look amongst them for a metaphor; the children's classics provide all that is needed. What more stark example of the effect a new woman can have upon a man is there than that in the desolate tale of "Hansel and Gretel"? Or the jealousy of an older woman whose beauty is crumbling in "Snow White"? What more profound guideline for living than Mrs Doasyouwouldbedoneby in "The Water Babies", or pragmatic living in "Pollyanna"? I can hear now the terror in the voice of Bluebeard's wife as she calls: "Sister Anne, Sister Anne, is there anybody coming?" I weep, and not like the Walrus, to think how many children miss out on these microcosms of the life ahead.

Anyhow, "The Princess and the Pea" is a short little tale, and somewhat odd. I don't think it is very well known and I hope I am remembering it correctly: a couple want the best, in their estimation, wife for their son, a girl from an aristocratic background, used to the finer things in life. He brings quite a few girls home to meet his parents and they always give her a room with a bed piled high with mattresses, about twelve of them, and underneath the bottom of the stack they place a dried pea.

Eagerly they await the girl's presence at the breakfast table: "How did you sleep, my dear?" "Like a log, thanks" - if this was the cheery answer then she was out on her ear.

At last a frail girl arrived in a storm, wet hair clinging to her head, and the usual bed was proffered. Next morning: "How did - " "Oh, I had a terrible night, didn't sleep a wink! There was something ghastly and lumpy under my mattress!" (I used to think she was rather rude. Why didn't she keep a stiff upper lip? And I wondered too how on earth she got on to that bed, did they provide a step ladder?) With joy, the complaining one was welcomed into the family: a pukka lady with delicate and refined sensitivities; a princess indeed, used only to the best. I do not remember whether they 'lived happily ever after'.

So now it seems not only are we members of the intelligentsia, but we have leanings towards the aristocracy too, ho hum. Very frequently I am the

Princess and the Pea Person, and excruciating it can be. Your sensitivity is raised to such a level that everything hurts: your watch strap, your hairpins, the collar of your jacket, your shoes, very much your shoes. And if you have a headache it is a very bad headache; whatever little pain you might have is emphasised cruelly.

But I have learnt now not to take pain killers if this is a time I am likely to be under-medicated. Wait till the L-dopa moves in and the scene is very different, perhaps just a little headache niggling away, nothing really. And if you regarded pain as a warning then you might be alarmed, but do not be, it is just the absence of your own home-grown dopamine that is causing all this. Apparently dopamine is the pain suppressor—and as that's not working, you get pain. *Not a lot of people know that!* And while it doesn't do a lot for the current discomfort, at least you know it will go away and that the shrill voices of aristocratic tendency are of no import.

Here's another '*not a lot of people know that*': not a tribulation but it needs to be said somewhere as it can make a real difference to how you feel. This concerns when you take your pills, particularly L-dopa. Ideally, it should be taken an hour before eating to achieve maximum efficiency, the more especially if protein is on the menu; protein destroys your medication!

You may be told at first to take the pills with food, this is just because it will help the ensuing possible nausea; as soon as that is resolved, get them right away from food. Time and again - I feed rather a lot of people and am not very good at being punctual - I find meal time and pill time coincide and I agonise over which to delay—and then end up by combining them with sorry results. Like being totally unable to help with the washing up.

Micrographia belongs in this category of tribulations, but I should also have put it under symptoms, for it is one of the first to appear and can be a warning indication to those who know. Your writing gets smaller and smaller until it's hardly there at all. Some years ago I had a lunch party for twenty-two women, they came from all over the place so lots of introductions would be needed. As usual, I made a list of them all and who I wanted to introduce to whom, and why; just an indication of mutual interest. The day came and after my first gulp of sparkling wine I went to look for said list; the information was writ so small I couldn't begin to read it and, alas, that day had to rely on my memory, much more taxing and unrelaxing.

And another little one. The time will come when people will say to you, "Had a swim, have you?" or "Have you just washed your hair?" Alack, all you've done is dead-head the roses. The slightest exertion causes your head to sweat. Bizarre, isn't it?

When I think of the following all-too-common complaint, I am reminded of a little piece from "Macbeth": one of the "black and evil midnight hags" senses Macbeth's approach across the blasted heath and cries: "By the pricking of my thumbs, something wicked this way comes!" Well, I cry "By the curling of my toes, PD comes and comfort goes!" (Or something like that; suggestions would be appreciated). Comfort certainly does go: those poor and somewhat exhausted toes are tightly curled and shoes become definitely surplus to requirements; off with them! Walking is a painful and tottering business, especially as the rest of the legs follow the lead: knees stick together in an extraordinary fashion and will not straighten. In my case, at least, a painful ache overcomes my legs. We're in for a stuck time and just hope a comfortable chair is nearby.

However, as I mentioned earlier, we have discovered a very freakish little assistance in this instance, and that is to walk sideways, crab-like to your destination, one leg torn from its magnetic-like position with the other, and carefully crossed right over and foot placed on the floor beyond. Hopefully it will be on the floor and not on the first foot. And you do have to be very careful about this manoeuvre because it is dangerously easy to fall.

I only do it when someone is with me and holding my hands to help me to wherever, walking backwards themselves—or sideways on this occasion. It is very strange how this seems to free everything up a little. I went through a phase when I couldn't think without crossing my legs; I felt quite desperate and claustrophobic if I was, say, sitting at a table which did not allow room for crossed legs underneath. Near panic gripped me.

And the crossed-legs-parade reminds me of another little possible move to outwit Parkinson's. I realised, late in the day, that when I was in the grip of the Giant Hand that I stopped breathing. Or very nearly. It was all so overwhelming that I almost gave up. Now to fight that, by learning how to breathe properly, perhaps a Yoga course or somesuch, gives you much more control and self-confidence. It will diminish, that fearful squeeze, and you will emerge in one piece.

I stopped driving about seven years ago. Professor

Lees advised me to when I went on the Ropinirole because it could cause little instant blackouts (I really like that pill otherwise, though half an hour after I take one I yawn and yawn fit to disjoint my jaw). In fact, I had already done so after twice finding myself on the grass verge without knowing how I had got there. Funny thing was, it was exactly in the same place and a very quiet rural road; I couldn't help wondering if it was something to do with ley lines, which are very plentiful in that area - though I haven't the faintest idea what they are. Also I had had a driving aberration which I didn't like: it seemed always that the car was pulling me into the middle of the road, I had to pull down on the left of the steering wheel hard and constantly. I had the car checked for tyre imbalance: they were fine. Other people have corroborated this one with me.   To be without your car, though, is a loss of freedom that many are reluctant to take.

I knew someone, husband of a friend, who had "Parkinson's in Denial".   I believe this is not uncommon, especially among men.   He'd been diagnosed and given the L-dopa pills which he took freely, as and when he felt one would be a help. The result was massive shaking, dyskinesia, and he needed three people to hold him still when he had an injection. One day he drove into the local town to visit the Halifax Building Society. Only trouble was, he forgot to get out of the car first. Straight in through the plate glass window. Armed police were on the scene almost immediately, this was surely a ram raid? "Actually," said the manager ruefully, "he's our best customer."

Here's another bizarre tribulation, spooky as well. About two years into Parkinson's, officially, Peter and I were on holiday in Greece and having the two-day seaside bit that was as much as he could stand before we fled to the mountains and a diminution of our fellow men. I took ten breast strokes and then, whoosh! Some unseen malevolent creature tugged my head down into the water and at the same time my legs shot up.

The first time it happened I was out of my depth and it was all pretty alarming. I never went out of my depth again, and on family holidays in Wales have my own inner tube, but it was invariable: ten strokes and you were looking into Davy Jones' Locker.

The story following is just hearsay but I have been told of a man with PD, holidaying in the Caribbean with his boat, who attempted to swim ashore, not a long exercise. He was wearing a life jacket yet he drowned. Those malevolent fingers must have a lot of strength and determination.

I had encountered them before, in milder form, when I was playing tennis, which I managed to continue with in the early years. Towards the end of the session I would feel those little fingers trying to get a hold on my shoulder blades, trying to tweak me backwards. Rather like your neurologist, testing your balance, but with more malice aforethought.

Extraordinary, truly bizarre, that hunched shoulders and stooping as we may be, yet we fall over backwards! What can it be but evil fingers tormenting our balance? I have seen one poor elderly man fall backwards three times: he is walking, shuffling rather, gently towards us and then suddenly flat on the ground on his back, and his frail wife and I unable to gather him up. I have only really fallen once. On the bonfire heap. I was scaling it with the cat litter tray in my hand to empty it on the summit. As I started to keel over I had this dread vision of the contents of the tray showering back upon me. To my infinite satisfaction I managed to hurl it away from me and my pleasure at this manoeuvre blotted out measuring my length in the ashes. But this is a nasty and dangerous side effect to put up with—or "up with which we will not put", to quote Churchill. And we need some of his tenacity, to guard against falling.

Small children are so very sweet and wanting to help, I find—and I am so afraid of squashing them. What do you do when a small hand is put out to help you? You just cannot dash chivalry on the head. I sometimes find it expedient to change my mind about getting up and journeying to the door, or the loo or wherever. I sit there in some discomfort and then, if I can get them to leave the room on some pretext, make a dash for it. "Dash" indeed! And I am rewarded for being in medicated good form too: "You are doing very well, Grandma," says my little three year old grandson approvingly. "You are taking nice big steps like me."

So there I am, to get back to cars et al, being driven around by my speedy sons. But they are good drivers and I don't really need to keep my eyes shut most of the time. But I do it because I think "We can't get through there! It isn't wide enough! We can't, we can't!" Which would be pretty boring for the driver as we glide easily through wherever. Our spatial powers are under attack. Ever noticed how frequently we barge into one side of a doorway when there is plenty of room for us to go through more elegantly?

A last oddity for now, although I am sure there are lots more lurking about. Perhaps other people could tell me, if I canvassed them? After all, the onlooker sees most of the game. Possibly a Case for Carers? Anyhow, this bizarre tribulation is my trouble with the telephone, and I think it is really a matter of low energy. Such low energy. In the afternoons particularly I turn the house upside down looking for chocolates, believing in their spurious ability to get me going. I think when I am talking to people in person, as it were, I pinch some of their magnetic forcefield, and get by on that—but on the telephone it is out of reach. I find I am screwing up my eyes, squirming in my seat (if I am not stuck) and the fingernails of the hand holding the receiver leave marks on my face, all in an effort to visualise the person I am talking to; we don't realise how much conversation bounces off what we perceive by body language. My idea of a good telephone call from a friend is "I'm just coming round to see you. 'Bye!"

Lying back comfortably against a small cloud
(page 76)

Chapter Seven

Complementary Therapies

This is something I am rather proud of: I have only been to see my GP once in the last thirteen years. And that was only for an ankle x-ray. I like to think that in this small way I am putting something back into the NHS, saving their services in exchange for so much that I take out: my visits to the neurologist twice yearly, my bags and bags and bags full of medication, that unopened I could pile around the house and make a sizeable barricade, indeed an imposing one.

Now this does not mean that there is never anything wrong with me, though actually, apart from Parkinson's, not a lot. It just means that I have invested in the alternative therapies. As I said before, they do not do anything about PD per se, but they manage to keep me in the good health that is needed to resist the malady and also to lessen the impact of the medication side effects. Did you know, that in ancient days in China you only paid your acupuncturist if you were well? If you were ill it was his fault for not keeping you in that splendid condition that repelled poor health, in other words your immune system should sparkle. It was truly a preventative system; you went three times a year whatever, in order to keep the body honed.

There are quite a few alternative or complementary therapies available: homeopathy, acupuncture, cranial and sacral osteopathy, Bowen Therapy, Reiki, reflexology. When I was first diagnosed, thirteen years ago, a dear and generous friend took me for about ten treatments to a Faith Healer. He'd had quite a number of amazing successes and was an honest and inspired man. It was pleasant to sit there in the gentle light, almost asleep, while his hands passed back and forth over me, never touching but exuding a faint warmth. It didn't do anything at all for me but afterwards we went to a tea shop and ate outrageous cakes (right from the beginning I boobed in thinking Parkinson's automatically ensured a slim figure) and then sat on the stony beach looking at the grey sea that surged against the Kentish coast. It was a pleasant jaunt from beginning to end, the car ride gave me a blissful sleep that eluded me at night, and the company of a best old friend was just what the doctor would have ordered, probably.   But PD reigned supreme.

There are lots of treatments and lots of people, you just have to keep experimenting to find what suits you; there is always something that does. Like when you come to treatments for arthritis, listen to this delectable one: "fill a jar with raisins, the best organic ones, then pour in gin up to the brim and leave for a week, thereafter eat nine raisins a day." Would you believe that works wonderfully well for some people? I know; I have met them—and aren't they the lucky ones. It has to be worth a try.

Homeopathy I have never tried, but I have a great respect for it from a distance. It is so very good for animals, a fact which can be used to confound those annoying people who sigh in a superior way and murmur "Well, I suppose if you believe..." They, you will notice, unfortunately for them, have such strong minds, minds that cannot be twisted to superstitious behaviour, that homeopathy is powerless to help—and they do not get around to putting it to the test.   Reiki I have not experienced either, only when it was focused on a close friend from a distance. Impressive it was, but then also it can be labelled as coincidence. I suppose I ought to totter off and join the ranks of annoying people.

Three people I am very fond of, quite separately from each other, had written to me over the years ardently encouraging me to seek help from the Bowen Therapy, a fairly new outfit started by an Australian of that name. It had been most effective for them and I always meant to have a try. When one of those kind friends died I felt guilty that I had never done as she requested, and then gone back to her with excited gratitude perhaps. So I gave it a try.

Bowen Therapy is a funny one and no mistake: tedious and bitty for the practitioner, I would have thought. I lay on the practice bed and she gently pressed some small and insignificant muscle, the same both sides, then exited for two minutes so I could relax in private. This happened about twenty times in a session, in and out that door, shutting it softly behind her. What do you do with a scant two minutes? Count? Like you do at bus stops when there isn't the time or opportunity to do anything worthwhile? A couple of press ups? Peel one potato? And yet, I was just discussing this treatment with a frequently visiting friend and she said: "Remember that first appointment? It was amazing. I'd never seen such a change in you. I felt I was seeing you without Parkinson's for the first time ever" (she being the best of chums but only three or four years old, if you get my drift.).

Something made me feel confident about this treatment and I put my two favourites on hold for a couple of months while I went fortnightly, but after a while I realised things were getting worse. This might sound a bit facile, but the nice practitioner agreed with me: there was an uncomfortable confrontation, meaning that the Bowen method firmly told my body how to respond, but Parkinson's already held that role and was not going to give up; they strove and guess-who was winning. And I was unfortunately the battleground. Regretfully I abandoned that treatment. Which doesn't mean to say it was not an excellent regime if Parkinson's were not in the ring.

The urge to sleep was so tremendous
(page 80)

Chapter Eight

Tried And Trusted (By Me)

So, back to my tried and trusted favourites, who were perfectly tolerant of my absence. Acupuncture had been part of my life for twenty odd years, so I'll talk about Cranial Osteopathy first. I had been to ordinary osteopathy once and vowed never again. Just that I am a wimp; I know this excellent and long established discipline has had endless successes, but I simply hated the sudden and unexpected seizing and twisting of my neck with a loud crack, and that a routine event.

Fear not with this refined variety. It consists of the laying on of fingertips, so lightly that it is easy to think they are not there at all, that that nice, amiable practitioner has popped out for a beer. But open your eyes and there he is, thoroughly intent and purposeful, fingers either side of your neck more often than not. And lying on that hard massage bed is heaven. There was a picture in my childhood book of the Greek Myths showing Psyche lying back comfortably against a small cloud and floating blissfully through the air; that's exactly what it felt like. For the first several years after diagnosis the only times I ever stopped shaking, or being in wretched discomfort with rigidity, was when I was lying on that inhospitable-looking couch. And then the colours that illuminated the insides of your eyelids! There was pale azure blue, sea green and, best of all, a heavenly apricot: that appears to me to be the colour of bliss, not easily attained.

The finger tip control required for this treatment is not as simple as it looks. The founder of this method trained his fingers to feel a hair through fifteen sheets of paper. With this measure of involvement they are able to move the spinal fluids around to bring the whole system into harmony. Harmony is the name of the game. The central nervous system wants to roll you into a ball, I believe, if you have Parkinson's that is.

If you bumped into me in the middle of the night, tottering to the loo, you would get a nasty shock: a little old bent-double crone, whose eyes can only look at the floor because the head points downwards. Between 10 pm and 6 am I am supposed to be without medication and that's when the demons rule. Luckily so far I have been able to make it to the adjacent loo, but I dare not trek any further, say to the kitchen for a comforting biscuit (and a good thing too!) because I would probably be cast to the floor with a dystonia in my foot.

And yet, withal, in between times I can stand up quite straight and even fool people into thinking I have PD only mildly, or not at all. Who am I kidding? I am still smarting from an incident in the supermarket when I had mislaid my son and a kind woman was helping me (actually she was doing it) unpack my trolley while I sat on my lovely stick/stool. "Thank you so much," I told her, and, to explain my languor, confided "actually I have Parkinson's", to which the wretch replied: "I know". The fact that a nurse's uniform was to be glimpsed beneath her coat comforted me a little. I expect I look funnier (stiffer and more awkward) than I always realise, but family and friends do confirm that I look more as in days of yore than would be expected. Most of the time my face does not lose all mobility, which is a help.

Cranial osteopathy (you only have to see what it does

for babies to be its fan for life!) very much helps to keep me moving to the proper rhythms; to maintain, as far as possible, fluidity and ease.

Because you enjoy and use the alternative, or complementary, therapies, does not in any way imply that you distrust or dislike allopathy. Not a lot of people know that "modern medicine", "the doctor", "the NHS", call it what you will, this vast framework that defines our safe passage through life, has its own name. (It somehow seems rather cheeky, that this all-powerful, all revenue-swallowing machine were just a discipline like many another. But think on't). I think allopathy is absolutely fantastic. Think of post-accident surgery! Think of people being snatched from the jaws of death (but not the ones who then live on in cabbage-fashion as a result). Think of producing babies for barren women! There is so much to admire and to rely on. I am in awe of doctors and nurses, their training, their dedication, their calm and wondrous ability. But I also think we overwork them and the system.

My own preferred route is to turn to the alternatives for early symptoms and simple problems; only when they cannot cope would I go to the doctor. And that is a process I dread too: getting on the conveyor belt that will deliver you from one consultant to another, and perhaps from exploratory surgery to hospitalisation—when you could be lying on a couch feeling pampered and at ease and with all the time in the world to recount every little discomfort. I wonder how much it could ease the system too and diminish the endless injections of money?

Of course, my situation gives me rather a different slant on things from that of most people. I am not looking for longevity. It is actually something I dread. The thought of getting really old and feeble while the unpleasant symptoms of Parkinson's increase their tyranny. No thanks. I gave up years ago going for any of these health checks that are offered; I hope I would ignore warning signs if they come, extreme old age is not my goal. I would like to exit before my darling family and friends are tried to the limits. I've enjoyed myself so much I do not want to spoil things by staying on too long - which I am aware is usually one of my failings when I'm having a good time. However, after that brave talk I also have to admit that I do not, definitely do not, want pain. And I want some quality of life while I hang on here. So back to acupuncture.

I'm pretty sure that it was acupuncture that kept me from realising I had Parkinson's for so long. My main problem in those years was fatigue. And a dire lack of energy. I was very fortunate that it coincided with my not having the tremendous (and enjoyable) work load I had had for the previous twenty five years of adulthood. So it didn't show so much to other people, I just became "that sort of person", one who curled up in a ball and fell asleep whenever she got a moment, who sat down a lot and had very little ambition for the fast lane.

I remember one winter's day being out for a country walk with some visitors and our two goats, Love and Joy. The urge to sleep was so tremendous that I hung back a bit and then slipped behind a frosty bush and passed out on the hard ground. Luckily a couple of minutes could suffice in an emergency: down that rabbit hole, faster, deeper, deeper. As long as you got to that deep level of sleep the neurotransmitters could rearrange themselves and you had a fresh start. Until the next time.

During those ten years, looking back I can see that it was acupuncture that kept me going, kept me on a plateau. I went pretty regularly, about once a month I think. The consulting room was on the first floor of a big old house in Tunbridge Wells, the dear man would come down to meet me—and then dance back up the stairs ahead of me. It looked like dancing to me, he was so light on his feet, so buoyant, soundless.

I trudged heavily up after him, like my shoes were weighted down with lead, and so was my mind for that relatively short duration of the climb; the contrast between us forced me to realise the state I was in these days, normally I could turn a blind eye.

"Give me some energy!" I would beg as the needles were produced.

"I'll do what I can," he promised, "but you'll only use it up. You've got to learn to conserve it. You should always leave a little swishing around in the bottom of the barrel—but you run it dry every time."

By that time I was asleep, the blessed sleep of the massage couch. The needles slipped into place painlessly, or with a satisfying little electric shock, as if to announce that that was exactly where they ought to be. Afterwards there would be an oily back massage that wafted you out on an odorous wave of comfort and well-being. I went down those stairs a lot better than I came up them, but I suppose that is understandable. And as I went I would be making myself a mental list: tasks in order of importance that must be completed before that barrel ran dry again.

"I say, Smithers, come and look at this one!"
(page 93)

Chapter Nine

Various Imponderables

My health was good otherwise, except for one darn thing, and that one which acupuncture seemed increasingly unable to control. The dread migraine. Gradually they grew in rigour and frequency until I was having agonising ones lasting up to twenty four hours every week. Where next, I wondered, in trepidation? It did not occur to me at that time that the migraines enforced rest on me, I had to be on my bed, except for brief stumbles round the room in a desperate search for relief. Then, one time, a doctor cousin from New Zealand was staying.

"There's a very effective anti-migraine tablet just come on the market," he told me. "Go for it."

I went for it. And secured it without trouble. Now, whenever the familiar pre-migraine rumbles were felt, I took a pill, two pills and lay on my bed for an hour. Then, hey presto I was back to normal! It was bliss indeed. But, as my wise Peter often said, everything has an equal and opposite force. The tremor then emerged with a vengeance.

The tremor started in my legs, not obvious to others at first but my thighs throbbed with it. I went to the doctor. "I'm pretty sure what the trouble is," he said, "but I'd rather you went to someone who knows more about it than me. I think you should see a neurologist."

By the time I got an appointment, four months later, I was vibrating across the room. I had the uncomfortable feeling that I made others seasick by bobbing up and down in front of them as we spoke. "Are you on any medication?" the young houseman neurologist asked, on the occasion of that official diagnosis. There was nothing but the pill for the migraines as and when they were indicated. "Well, come off those immediately," he said in a very decisive manner. Interesting.

That first year after diagnosis I opted to go on a drug trial. And this had the pleasant outcome that I have stayed ever since under the care of Professor Andrew Lees' team of neurologists at the National Hospital in London; couldn't be bettered. And nice with it. During the year long drug trial I continued shaking heartily, and this had a useful side effect: I ate well and stayed comfortably slim. When you think of it, all that vibrating is like doing isometric exercises; one estimate that I heard a doctor had given was that such shaking was equal to walking ten miles.

Then, after a year (and, incidentally, I am sure I got the placebo because I noticed nothing at all happening but a steady decline), after that year – L-Dopa! What a difference! I can imagine the excitement when it was first discovered: Parkinson's very own drug. Two things almost immediately manifested: I could go to a concert or a lecture and not fidget! It had always been an embarrassment to me that I could not sit still and absorbed like other people, but must needs shift and wriggle, right leg over left, left leg over right like a naughty child. I now felt composed and dignified-- and grown up. And - the migraines ceased! It had been lack of dopamine that had caused them. And the more I pushed myself and struggled with that dire lack of energy, the more they laid me out. And apparently this was just the start of my honeymoon with L-Dopa, which should continue for five years.

That was eleven, twelve years ago. I will gloss over my foolish adventure that occurred about four years ago, one that I was much warned against by Professor Lees' team at the National. I made myself very ill by becoming a guinea pig for an American/Chinese Medicine experiment to cure Parkinson's. This involved cutting back on my medication in case I was actually beginning to manufacture dopamine myself again. Mustn't have too much; one can see the awful effects of that in "Awakenings". I think I got down to about one sixth of my original dosage. But it was all rather hazy, as well as horrid (the Giant Hand nearly made mincemeat of me). And by then I was incapable of looking after myself.

One good thing happened though, like little Hope flying out of Pandora's casket. Because I had been off my drugs for a while my body had had a rest from their attentions: the honeymoon was on again. After a polite and gradual reintroduction process, I was actually able to operate on less than I had had before. Rising steadily, of course, as time goes by (sounds like the Shipping Forecast, read by Judi Dench).

So I'm not really any worse than I was about six years ago; pretty jolly lucky and amazing. And I continue to go to acupuncture, about once a fortnight at the moment (and cranial osteopathy monthly). My health can't be too bad because despite my lack of sleep - I am fortunate if I get more than four hours, and very seldom more than two at a stretch - I do have bursts of energy. It is just one a.m. at the moment... And acupuncture offers another treat. I justify myself, as women will, that as I do not have holidays nor drive a car then I can indulge in these treatments. They have a centuries old cosmetic trick; they can tighten the little muscles of the face to counteract, just a bit, The Droop. That Dire Droop that makes a person look not only old and ill but also grumpy. And, whatever else I am, I am certainly not grumpy.

It occurs to me that I haven't really explained anything about these treatments: how, why and wherefore they work. That is because I don't know, but it doesn't really bother me; I don't want to have a dog and bark myself. All that matters is that it seems to work: the proof of the pudding is in the eating. I'm beginning to sound like The Older Generation when I was a child: conversation was by platitude. You could talk for ages bouncing off one aphorism on to another. It solved the problem of the grown-up's embarrassment at having to talk to a small person with a small brain that couldn't comprehend the wisdom of their elders and betters. Those lovely, floating collections of words still haunt me; I can spend a happy morning muttering to myself "If at first you don't succeed, try,

try again! Ouch! Ah me, it is a poor workman that blames his tools. After all, fools rush in where angels fear to tread. And a fool and his money are soon parted....." You get the gist? Yes, it is as plain as the nose on my face, early to bed and early to rise, makes a man healthy, wealthy and wise... And it is now two a.m. ......

. . . .

And now it is the next day, albeit night time. I suppose, being on the road now to being, just a little bit, healthier, wealthier and wiser, I should erase that last non-sequitur of a paragraph. But I don't want to. Late night musings and early childhood memories all have a bearing on how we cope with things. In lots of ways, while laughing at them, I have found those petty profundities of the past to be reassuring and helpful: "laugh and the world laughs with you, weep and you weep alone"; "life is only froth and bubble, two things stand like stone, kindness in another's trouble, courage in your own". We're getting into autograph book country now; not to mention "The Sound of Music" and its ilk. But "sufficient unto the day is the evil thereof" and I will get back on track.

I've been looking for somewhere to add another little *not a lot of people know that*. And this time it is about alternative medicine, literally, all those lovely herbal pills. Personally I should like to take the lot, every one of them appears to be applicable to my various shortages and failings. But perhaps one would wonder about the wisdom of trying them and question their validity? Well, Germany has done clinical trials to assess the efficacy of three of them, and if the Germans have done a clinical trial that is quite good enough for me. The ones they covered were Echinacea, St John's Wort and Gingko biloba. And now, apparently, German doctors prescribe them abundantly; as much, or more, St John's Wort is prescribed annually than Prozac (always scary taking the latter because it goes down on your medical records). Echinacea is a splendid champion of the respiratory system. More and more people take it into hospital with them to guard against the horrid possibility of contracting MRSA while they are there. And it really helps if you are prone to getting colds and sore throats.

But Gingko biloba is the pill par excellence. It has a lot of different effects, the main one being to nurture the brain. It is supposed to sharpen the intellect and improve the memory—and, do you know, I really believe it does. I'm sure I will always become colander-like when I am unmedicated, but the rest of the time I am not spending so long searching for that elusive word, or name. Not groping and saying "It begins with a "T", I think", when it turns out to be a "W". No, the wanted word slides smoothly on to my tongue. I sometimes think I am as good, in that area, as the Laymen (by which I mean those who are not members of the Parkinson's Club). And Gingko biloba is rumoured to help with tinnitus, too. Just suppose one had tinnitus *and* hallucinated. Doesn't bear thinking about. And actually, I meant "better than" and not "as good as".

The best outfits selling these products will have a panel of professionals who are there to give you advice and tell you if it is safe to take what you want alongside other medication. For instance, I believe St John's Wort is not advisable if you are taking certain heart pills. That seems to admit their effectiveness, doesn't it? Like the cartoon where the doctor is saying seriously to his patient: "Well, the medicine must be working - you have all the side effects."

The only other alternative discipline that I have tried is Reflexology, and that I have not given a fair trial. Simply because I already have the other two, acupuncture and cranial osteopathy, up and running at the same time. The friend who normally stays with me, to my enormous relief and satisfaction, a couple of days a week, is a practitioner of reflexology. She gives me a treatment when she can, and when neither of the other two have appointments in the immediate vicinity. It is bliss to have such a treatment; I go to sleep almost instantly and for the duration. But any long term effect is lost in the maelstrom of possible effects from the other two, combined with the obdurate unreliability of Parkinson's itself. Good days are random, as are bad ones, sometimes they come in groups, like the Number 11 bus (just occurred to me: how about a "bonus" of buses?); anything to confuse and make a nonsense of pet theories. This last time I felt terrible the following day, my legs ached so badly and I was exhausted and my colander of a head had done its fell deed. I wondered if it was similar to (my theory of) the Bowen Therapy: too confrontational with Parkinson's and causing me to take the flak for such insolence? Then today has been such a good one!

Those same legs (as I fondly call my tree trunks) have hardly ached at all and I've been in best form for a long time. Is it reflexology, at the hands of a particularly gifted practitioner, whom I must thank? The third day is traditionally the telling one with these sorts of disciplines; the intervening day often just leaves you feeling battered. Or, on the other hand, is it simply random? Who knows?

And then, who knows what happens in the world of

allopathy, our resident medicine either? At least, I expect most of the doctors and consultants do, with their supreme mastery of those long and alien names for inconspicuous-looking little pills - like characters in a Russian novel they always have to have at least two. But I certainly don't. To me it is all as mysterious as why telephones work, why computers work (sometimes), why, at the click of a camera, our environment can be fastened to a piece of paper, or a loved one's image for one fleeting moment secured forever.

I do have one criticism of the practitioners of conventional medicine, though, particularly in its higher reaches. It is a very minor one in the scheme of things, set against the miracles they perform. But betwixt the medical mind and the non-medical lies a giant divide, a ha-ha of epic proportions. In their dispassion they can have blind spots. For example, their inability to realise how PD is perceived by the man in the street, the afore-mentioned Dyna-rod man. I had another good example of this the other day.

Along with many others I have donated my brain to medical science. This is not as an organ transplant, as some people have sweetly assumed, but as something to take apart and scrutinise, in the desperate effort to unravel the mysteries of PD. We have done this donor-thing because we know how much our doctors need these appendages; we have been duly thanked and congratulated. Now, I'm pretty sure, most of us would prefer not to think about it again. We carry a card, we tell our GPs and our relatives that on our death this will need immediate attention. Our donation must be removed at top speed; we gulp and smile in a pleased way to hear that this will not be apparent from the front of the head. Our mindless visage can even be looked upon, should anyone actually want to do so.

End of story? But no, lest we think them ungrateful, our medical chums send out to us a six monthly newsletter. The latest one bears on its cover a picture of a brain (unlovely, rubbery thing), together with further details of the removal process. Which of us does not look upon it and blench? Return to sender, please...

Having mentioned the difference between our attitudes, I must just attend to another little side issue. In all its forlorn glory, suppose that little remnant of us should be found wanting? Suppose they titter? "I say, Smithers, come and look at this one! Are you sure it didn't belong to a pygmy?"

There was a cartoon once that I liked so much I

copied it on to a progress report I was doing for Professor Lees. I don't know whether he ever saw it. Or found it funny. A doctor is handing something to his seated patient, leaning across his desk: "And this is the result of your brain scan," the doctor says. The object he proffers is a piece of paper little bigger than a postage stamp. There, but for the Grace of God, go I.

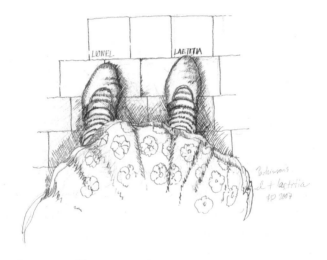

Eventually my right leg was christened Laetitia
(page 37)

Chapter Ten

Having It All? Hollow Laugh!

There used to be a little wartime hospital near us, a row of Nissen huts, built for the welfare of the Canadian soldiers who had come to help us fight against Germany. It must have been very inconvenient for the staff, having to go outside in the cold days of winter, to get into one of the other huts, each one being a ward, but I loved it. This was back in the Sixties and already it was considered to be a rackety disgrace, but it wasn't just me, I think everyone loved it; it had such a good atmosphere. There was nothing remotely high-tech about it, no gleaming polished corridors (which made you feel giddy if you were sick), just a lovely air of camaraderie. Somehow the hospital belonged to the staff, and to the patients too, not the other way round.

The devil...made disgusting noises
(page 99)

We were not overwhelmed or diminished by its spotless modernity - though I am sure it was a lot cleaner than hospitals today. It had to be: there were Matrons then! Here the wards were not numbered; they had idiosyncratic names.

Just as well I liked it as I had a series of operations here, during my late twenties. Only things like appendix and hernias, niggling little things but at least an opportunity for a good rest—they actually let you lie in bed a bit, and read a book sometimes. And once I had the excitement of behaving very strangely, after my appendix I think it was. I came round to find eight doctors ringing my bed, looking at me with great interest. I was in a rigor and with soaring temperatures. After more intriguing maladies had been exonerated it turned out to be a malarial attack. The odd part being that it was ten years since I had last had such a thing. But what I most remember was how everyone helped each other.

I came round, heavy with anaesthetic, to find a little old lady tottering (sounds like me nowadays!) towards me: "Hello, dearie, is there anything I can get you?" she said. I should hate to have a room to myself. Not only is there so much more scope for self pity, but there is no one to catch you in an emergency, to yell for help when you fall out of bed, or like a darling friend of mine, have dreadful and frightening cramps. The busy nurses cannot be looking in on lone patients all the time. No, you are safer in the ward. And there is the panoply of life to watch, not unlike sitting at a pavement cafe in Paris watching the world go by (miss the chestnuts in blossom, though). There was a woman who celebrated her fiftieth operation while I was there: she went into the theatre clutching a cake and champagne for the doctors! She was so brave and so stalwart. I went back to see her when I had recovered myself, but she had died.

However, the fellow patient I am really remembering at the moment was a gentle, undemanding woman in her fifties, perhaps. And this may sound quaint but what she said shocked me (can life really have changed so much in forty years!). She told me she lived alone! "You live alone?" I said incredulously. I had honestly not heard of anyone living on their very own; nowadays it seems half the population does. Poor woman! "But don't you get very lonely?" I asked, pressing the point rather tactlessly. "Oh, no, dear," she replied patiently. "There are some nice young children living next door, and sometimes I can hear them playing in the garden." The simplicity, and total lack of self pity, in that remark impresses me still.

I could never manage with so little contact with the rest of the world. Alack for my inadequacies. I need people to be fascinated by, to hug and be hugged by, to protect me with their snores from the menace of night time creaks and inexplicable noises. Particularly for us, with Parkinson's and the dangerous levels of nightmare and hallucination, it must be very alarming to live alone. One friend, about the same stage of PD as I am, wakes at night sometimes to find strange people standing around her bed. Imagine! I don't know why, but I've been lucky enough not to hallucinate so far; my fingers are firmly crossed. I've had nightmares all my life; one so dreadful - where the Devil sat beside my bed and made disgusting noises while he contemplated me, as if some glutton envisaging the meal he was about to gorge - that it caused me at the age of eighteen to leap out of my bed, tear down the passage and hurl myself into the bed of my astonished parents. When the Devil had removed himself, that is, I could not have stirred a muscle before. But I don't think I have any more nightmares nowadays than then, perhaps even fewer, though Nocturnal Nock, the son who is there for me in the night, says that sometimes I scream and he comes down to my bed in the sitting room and I am peacefully asleep again. He also tells me that before the scream I often howl like a wolf. I can understand that: I do howl when pain is too bad and I need to offload some of the strain I am feeling. A howl is rather satisfying, and more dignified than a yell. You have to imagine a frozen night, an icy white moon in the clear sky, the desolation of the empty prairie, and throw your head back...

Why are we so alone these days? A fantastic change in just the last four decades. I know that a lot of other nations, Filipinos and Indians for a start, marvel, in aghast fashion, at the way we treat our aged. With them, any old person is taken into the family, some family however extended. Jill Lowe, a friend who travelled in India and fell in love with the driver of the car she hired - then writing that rather fascinating book "Finding the heart of India" after she had married him - was telling me about her mother-in-law. The old woman, not so old really, probably in her fifties but looking in her eighties, had Alzheimer's. I commiserated strongly: poor Jill and everyone, how awful. "No, no!" cried Jill, "you don't understand, Sarah, it's not awful at all. It's no problem. She just sits on her charpoy outside her hut all day, occasionally she throws a plate or something, but it doesn't matter. It's just accepted. It's life; that's the way Life is!" She loved India dearly.

But I'm sliding away from the problem—what are we going to do with ourselves when we are old, old and feeble?   It would be nice if we could just automatically be found a little space of our own within our children's families.   Even moving around (ahem, being moved around) to spend a wadge of time with each child, should we be fortunate enough to have several - and we should be useful! Women want to be useful, even if we are just podding peas with slow, arthritic, Parkinsonian fingers, or watching baby and yelling for help when it awakes, or answering that inconvenient telephone: "Hello, speak up, dear, would you? Who? Say again...?"   So lovely to be needed; so lovely to have people around whom you can love.   Who was it moaned those words: "Something to love, Oh, something to love! Some tame gazelle..."

When there is no-one to love or need us we are to be found sitting in front of that bloated television, together with many of our ilk, watching with unseeing eyes some banal programme peopled by frenetic and farcical characters who have lost all meaning for us, if they ever had any.   The father of some cousins of mine had Parkinson's, and was eventually moved from his debris-strewn flat after the earthquake (at least, that is the impression it gave) to a last-stop nursing home. There he behaved with admirable pragmatism. He owned no television, that was non grata, but there was a good radio and a great many wonderful classic

CDs. And there were lots of bottles: gin bottles, whisky bottles and especially wine bottles. It was a constant party! The cleaners came to join in; the nurses when they went off duty; the doctors when they called; his visitors; other people's visitors. He died happily, merrily one almost might say, and somewhat prematurely. Which is fine by me, given the circumstances. He is much missed. Especially in a certain old folks' sunset home.

It is a pity we become so addicted to our own premises. I suppose it is the equal and opposite force of having the Good Life, of making beautiful habitats for ourselves that we cannot then bear to leave. I know it is as much the fierce independence of the elderly to want to carry on regardless, on their own until that final nasty fall precipitates dispatch to a Home (O, weasel word). And this clinging on, this escalation of folk living on their own is one reason why the multitude of houses, the concrete and tarmac, flourish in this land. If we want "the weeds and the wilderness yet" then children must stay home, unless employment calls from afar, until they get married (think how that would facilitate building up a nest egg!) and the elderly must retire gracefully to a corner of another's home.

There is a lovely little story amongst the collection of

those tales written by the Brothers Grimm. An old man lives with his son and daughter-in-law, but he has become a messy eater (sound familiar?) and is banished to a little stool in the corner, with his wooden bowl. He is broken-hearted at this exile, the shame and humiliation. One day his little grandson comes in with some wood and a collection of wood-working tools.

"What are you doing, my love?" enquires his fond mother. "What are you turning your clever little hands to now, my son?"

"Oh, mother dear," replies the child. "I am just making bowls for when I am grown to be a man, and when you and my father come to live with me, and sit on your little stools to eat your food."

The old father is reinstated.

I'm busy making bedrooms in my house. I sleep now in the sitting room, since 'sleep' has lost its meaning, and I am too gregarious to be happy on the periphery of events. That means that my bedroom, the one I shared with my husband, is up for grabs. And that room next to the kitchen, where the children played, and where the toys could lie thick upon the carpet without recrimination, that makes a pretty bedroom.

The ideal one for people who cannot get up the stairs easily - like my brother when he breaks a leg. He hasn't done it yet and I don't like to put ideas into his head, but it can only be a matter of time.

I have this dream: that my elderly kith and kin, when they cannot manage to live on their own any more— come to live with me. What fun we shall have! One of us, I am sure, will be able to read, another to hear, one will have fingers that can accomplish little tasks, it is not beyond conceiving that we will be able to play a few card games or patience, or we could throw beanbags at each other. The prospect of all the fun things we can do is impressive; I think I shall start making a list right now.

But the great conclusion is that, because we help ourselves and each other as much as possible, we will not need a one-to-one carer ratio. Think what a saving that will be! Because carers (and why should they?) do not come cheap. Roughly they cost the same as being in a nursing home. But they have so much more to recommend them: we are at home, our home, and in control basically—and so we do not have to eat our final meal at half past five in the afternoon and be in bed by six: "And does it not seem hard to you, when all the sky is clear and blue, And I should like so much to play, To have to go to bed by day." We have arrived at second childhood with a vengeance, once we cross the threshold of a Home.

It has become so habitual nowadays to put one's aged parents in a Home that I wonder whether people have really thought it through and examined the alternatives. Someone confided in me, with a certain wryness, that his mother in law had got through all the money that he had expected would be left to his wife. Ten years in a Home at £500 a week. "Tot that up!" he said. But I was totting other things: she was such a very harmless old lady, the last person in the world to throw her weight around, why could she not have come to live with them? If there was not all that much room, then some of her money could be invested in buying a larger property. A little more money could be spent in having a nice kind person come in and do things for her from time to time. Wouldn't she love to watch her grandchildren grow? As much as she would be horribly embarrassed by their being dragged to see her in the aforesaid Home. "When can we go home? When can we go home? It's boring here!" And indeed it is, with the best will in the world from the staff and board of governors.

This quiet and gentle old lady had a loving family, between them they came to see her every day of the week. There wasn't much to do: the old lady sat and stared at the wall, they sat and stared at the old lady. And sometimes at the wall. To me it appeared that she had a thought balloon drifting above her head, "What is wrong with me that my sons and daughters would rather spend £500 irrecuperable pounds a week - money we saved for them with infinite love and frugality - than have me to live with them?" A poser indeed.

Banished to a little stool
(page 103)

Chapter Eleven

Coping With Carers

But I have at last come to carers. And what a growth industry! They flock here from abroad to look after ageing Britons. Privately they roll their eyes at the eccentricity of the English and others who have lost that fierce family feeling, and, apparently, a proper regard for family money. Some of the loveliest and best of the carers come from far off countries to which their families had emigrated, I hear. It warms the cockles of one's heart to hear how ideal it is for them: women in their fifties perhaps, who come over to the old country to see their long lost relatives and stay a few days with them in between the serious business of looking after rich and helpless old people, mainly women. It's like magic, for when they return home

"Thank you, Mr Atkins, when the guns begin to play"
(page 117)

that money will be increased tenfold by the rate of exchange.

I had carers for the best part of a year—and it was the best part of a year, because they were all so marvellous that really it would be unseemly to say much about them (if you are a very lucky person you have to learn not to brag about it too much).   They came because at that time I was ill and incapable as the result of going on that aforementioned experiment, one that emanated from America and one that a great deal of dedicated research had gone into.   It was not in any way a scam; it just didn't work if you were already well launched into Parkinson's, and they warned you strongly of this.   It might still work one day, I believe; they thought they had found the cause, which is a good start.   And they thought they could get the dopamine to flourish again, hence the necessity of cutting back the medication.

I wouldn't have gone on this trial if allopathy, and The National Hospital for Neurology, had had something for a born-again guinea pig, but it seemed I was not to be indulged any longer.   I had done a couple of brain scans and a few other minor things, and they seemed to think it was enough for one person.   But, as many people must feel, it is dreary to have something amiss without making some effort to correct it.   To be having a beastly time and no good coming out of it, that offends any properly pragmatic Parkinsonian. Buck passed to allopathy!

Be that as it may, it all tended to go as they had predicted: I was ill from the diminution of my medication—but particularly ill from the withdrawal symptoms. Apparently we are given, and this is in no way a complaint, some of the most addictive drugs there are. We are not normally expected to come off them so it doesn't matter; I am quite chuffed to think I got as far as I did, though I certainly cannot boast of Cold Turkey.

My first carer came from an agency. It was a bit of an emergency because suddenly my legs wouldn't work at all, and so family swooped and in no time at all there was this delightful young woman coming from somewhere nice and hot, via a local agency. She was delightful because she was so kind and so affectionate; one couldn't exactly call her efficient. The second day I was sitting on a chair in the sitting room, all sounds very correct, ready to have a strip wash, at which she excelled.   It took a couple of hours or more but she rendered it free of embarrassment, which was a good start. Suddenly I felt a mug of warm water being poured over my head, to repose soggily on the only carpet we had ever bought new. I had mentioned that sometime I would like to have my hair washed, but I had imagined a little more preparation.

If I asked her to fetch me something from the third drawer down of the dressing table in my bedroom, I would hear her emptying cupboards in the kitchen; something from the office would necessitate a prowl in the garden shed. Perhaps she could cook? What do you mostly eat in your country, she was asked, she was a fairly new arrival. "Maize", she replied. "And what else do you cook?" "Maize," she insisted, and would not be persuaded to elaborate. She had to go, the little love, not really because of these shortcomings, I'm sure we would have improved things given time, but because she was so expensive, coming from an agency.

After that it was a melange of family and friends. Because of them I remember that near year with great affection. I often felt very ill and had all sorts of strange sensations. There was formication, for instance. This is because it feels as if ants are at work under your skin, a horrid sensation and in my case I visualised them as maggots, which is even more distasteful. It gave you sort of panic attacks, which I had not had before, but it was then that I proved to myself that Rescue Remedy, Bach's floral emergency, really does work: a few drops on the tongue and you could cope a lot better. I daresay the population of Cornwall were told that I was having a bad time with fornication (note the subtle exchange of n for m), thus paving the way for the later affliction of necrophilia.

Frequently I felt so dreadful, mainly the extreme rigidity, I think, but with all sorts of little extras, and then I had this compulsion to lie face down on the floor. It was the only thing; that was where I had to be. Ridiculous that it can be so difficult to get down on the floor. My knees were swollen and very painful, a pile of cushions had to be heaped, stepwise, to help me lower myself. Ten minutes was the most I could stay down there, and yet somehow it did, indeed, help. Getting back up again and into my chair (which, incidentally, is the dearest sanctuary of a chair. I think I'll be buried in it. Except that I want to be cremated) was very arduous and never a foregone conclusion.

Looking back, and looking around me too, I can see that there will always be some small amount of friction between the carer and the cared for. This is over how much you do. In my case it was because they thought I did too much. "There," they would cry, "you see, you did do too much, I warned you this would happen!" It was not so, I do not think. You just have to push yourself; if you don't that ol' wheelchair will get you. It'll get you anyhow, but I mean prematurely. One of my sons was telling the neurologist from Professor Lees' team that I did, or tried to do, too much. "Good," he replied. "Good. Well done. Keep it up."

Besides, Parkinson's is too slippery an affliction to be comprehended like that: you are not better or worse because of anything you have done. It asserts itself as and when it will. A few good days and you've feverishly worked out the answer: "it must be that papaya I ate!" and, *whoosh* down that snake you go again. But there is more to it than that, this slight bossiness of the carer. I think it comes from frustration: they want you to get better, they want to feel they can outwit this illness, that they hold the key; that under their care you can get better. Alack, you cannot; they are there for purposes of amelioration and stretching out your days upon this earth. As pleasantly as possible. Which in my case, was very pleasantly (but just don't let them catch you struggling to get out of your chair without ringing your little bell first...).

And there is something else to beware of. I did not experience this because my cared-for sojourn was not long enough, but I can see it and feel it, and understand it, I think. It will be impossible for them not to become a bit irritated with you at times, because you do not get better. "You even have the nerve to get worse!" they are thinking subliminally. "Now it is in the nature of things that you get better; you work at it, do as you are told, and you get better. It is really rather tedious of you to keep up this charade." Don't we all feel that, too? Particularly with something like Parkinson's which covers such a wide field of sensation: sometimes you feel quite good! You forget about the horrid bits - and then there they are again. Hard not to feel your willpower is weak. Like Peter walking on the water, you cannot keep it up.

And nobody can really share it with you, not even your best beloved. I see now why some people talk too much about their health problems and the minutiae of their symptoms, it is so you can understand what they are putting up with. It can be quite peeving to be really brave, go into overdrive, which is exhausting, and try like mad to pretend you are not feeling dire, only to have your healthy, gullible carers presuming that there is nothing wrong.

"You *have* had a good day, haven't you!"

Have you noticed how much easier it is to be strapped

up with a broken leg and bandages galore, than have a sickness working within you? With the first disability, maybe not even hurting too badly, you can relax; your garb says it all. But no, this is one of those dragons, one that must be studied very carefully and the peculiarities of its menace noted. Why do you mind if your efforts to rise above your situation convince too well? Is it because although you may not wince or grimace or grumble, you are still not your old self; you probably, quite understandably, appear dull and faded. Is it really a matter of self-esteem? You want, still, excuses to explain yourself. So perhaps you fall back on explanations of your symptoms and discomforts. That is boring and a big mistake.

There is a way out and that is to bask sometimes in the company of those in a likewise condition. The joy of discussing all the little details without being a bore - being, in fact, illuminating: "Oh, you haven't yet? It'll come! It'll come!" "And the worst bit is...", "And do you this and do you that?" Bliss. I suppose it is something like being a Mason; with your peers of that realm you share extraordinary things and events.

Outside you keep absolutely mum. Yes, that's the way to do it. I don't believe that you always have to say "Fine, thank you," when asked. You can, if it is so, say "Crumby, actually." And then probably add, "but I shall feel better in due course," and change the subject. The important thing is not to linger on your plight.

But I am frightened, frightened in case I cannot maintain these things that I have just been harping on about. The people who care for me are the ones I care most about: my darling, kind and inspirational family and friends. At the beginning I promised myself that I would on no account be grumpy. You see it all too often, when the sick person vents his (or her) frustration and unhappiness on those who look after him. It's totally illogical - and a barrier to getting the best help. I so very much hope I will not let them down, or myself. I have noticed that when I feel my worst, a dreadful aching round the centre of my body and my legs, the Giant Hand wringing me out, that I am devoid of a sense of humour. A smile by no means comes naturally; I am, inside, a real old misery, even if I don't spell it out. I have to find some way of rising above it.

We all have our role models, I have several and marvel at them. But there is one category of unknowns that really call me to order: soldiers. Tommy Atkins, the one who complained, quite legitimately, in Kipling's poem "It's Tommy this and

Tommy that and Tommy go away..." But it's 'Thank you, Mr Atkins' when the guns begin to play." All those scraps of documentaries we have seen of them in the First World War, grey faced and quietly determined, faithful defenders of our freedom. They may have been gung-ho in the beginning but now they accept where they are, not just as themselves but as part of a whole. And perhaps we are all too aware of ourselves as individuals, when in reality we are just Shakespeare's poor players, strutting and fretting in a world of chaos; one full of extraordinary sufferings. All that matters is how we conduct ourselves. That alone justifies our existence.

I think I'm lecturing myself into a better state of mind. Throw in a bit of Pollyanna and I'll be susceptible to hope! And here is one lovely thing, it was at this time I discovered the power emanating from being read poetry to. I expect that in many people's experience it would be music or looking at art perhaps, that would lift them out of the misery of extreme discomfort, but in mine it is the music of words. It was then I decided as a project to collect together my own anthology, so that I could be read to at any time without encountering a poem I did not like. My darling carers, whichever one found themselves stuck with me, helped with enthusiasm: they searched through great and respectable anthologies and followed up red herrings offered by others. What I wanted was poems of which I knew and remembered a line or two, a wisp of a thought, poems that I sincerely wanted a better acquaintance with. And in they rolled; I could have made a fatter book, but I am content.

Now I can always have beautiful, meaningful words rolling around in my brain, even when that is a colander, even when nothing else seems to be there. This week I have had "the glamour of childish days is upon me". And there has been "the feet of children pushing Yellow leaves along the gutter In the blue and bitter Fall...". And, listen: "The angels keep their ancient places, Turn but a stone and start a wing, 'Tis ye, 'tis your estranged faces That miss the many-splendoured thing."

"Turn but a stone and start a wing...."
(page 118)

Chapter Twelve

Laughter And The Love Of Friends

And that brings me to something else, lines from a poem by Hilaire Belloc:

"From quiet homes and far beginnings
On to the undiscovered ends,
There's nothing worth the wear of winning
But laughter and the love of friends."

I know I can be flippant about Parkinson's and I hope I do not offend anyone, but if we can't be, who can? The poor public has to be sympathetic whatever. But I also have to confess it is easier for me than most, it would be ungrateful not to do so. First of all I became embroiled with PD at the optimum age: I was still needed, perhaps, but I certainly wasn't indispensable.

Perhaps our smiles and looks of astonishment
and gratification are hanging in trees somewhere?
(page 123)

I'd had the most delightful life anyone could imagine and had felt nervous for some time that the gods would notice and my hubris cause a lightning bolt.

As lightning bolts go there are worse, far, far worse. My darling husband died, but it was as and when he would have wished to go. And I would not wish to linger either, and have made a Living Will to that end (and then my porous, leaky brain can go to the National Hospital with my blessings.) I live in a house I love, without real financial anxiety, and have a garden to die for (or to die in, if one tries to keep up with it. Better I make it into a wood). But best of all is Hilaire Belloc's laughter, and the love of friends and family.

Nocturnal Nock, the son who lives here with me, is there whenever I am awake at night or in pain or discomfort. He does the crossword puzzle with me, reads to me good books - and I am the only PD person I know who is not deliciously slim. Alack - only at the time I do not feel "alack" enough - that I am proffered strawberry ice cream cornets, toasted fruit bread and even (on Tuesdays) cream cakes, irresistible in the middle of the night for their contraband, forbidden feast essence. I know it is a very different story for many, but I still think that if we can dredge up any reason for laughter, then it is a little easier.

No one makes me laugh more than my son William. We were in town one day and I was trying to get out of the car but was jammed. "Pull my leg please, William." I said. "You're a fat old cow!" he responded obediently, and on top note. Nearby strangers looked askance and with pity as the unkind man helped his poor old mother out of the car, she having become a wobbling jelly not immediately identifiable as an elderly woman in a fit of giggles.

I have been feeling for some time that a key to Parkinson's lay in "Alice in Wonderland" and also "Alice through the Looking Glass ". Certainly the rabbit hole, falling down thereof, was an immediate metaphor that fitted perfectly. Then, when I have been incarcerated by rigidity in my armchair for some time, and painfully and with difficulty stand up, then it seems to me that I go on and on uncurling; I am enormously tall. I can't look down at the carpet: it will give me vertigo. And isn't that what happens to Alice when she's forever nibbling bits of this and that to get herself in or out of places, or sipping from bottles labelled "Drink Me"? Then the Cheshire Cat, is he not a cunning manifestation of face and expression being parted? Like us poor things who cannot smile or express in our faces what we are thinking because of the muscles' locking device. Perhaps our smiles and looks of astonishment and gratification are hanging in trees somewhere?

How nice it would be if the caterpillar sitting on the mushroom, engrossed in his hookah, was a metaphor for a neurologist. I looked through Alice's first interview with this character:

"Who are you?" said the Caterpillar.
This was not an encouraging opening for a conversation. Alice replied rather shyly, "I – I hardly know, Sir, just at present—at least I know who I was when I got up this morning, but I think I must have been changed several times since then."
"What do you mean by that?" said the Caterpillar sternly. "Explain yourself!"
"I can't explain myself, I'm afraid, Sir," said Alice, "because I'm not myself, you see."
"I don't see," said the Caterpillar.
"I'm afraid I can't put it more clearly," Alice replied very politely, "for I can't understand it myself to begin with; and being so many different sizes in a day is very confusing."
"It isn't," said the Caterpillar.
"Well, perhaps you haven't found it so yet," said Alice, "but when you have to turn into a chrysalis - you will some day, you know—and then after that into

a butterfly, I should think you'll feel it a little queer,
won't you?"
"Not a bit," said the Caterpillar.
"Well, perhaps your feelings may be different," said
Alice: "all I know is, it would feel very queer to me."
"You!" said the Caterpillar contemptuously, "Who
are you!"

No, I don't think so. Not like any neurologist I have
met. Could they have been like that a hundred years
ago (Lewis Carroll's book was first published in
1865)? I doubt it (and I will refrain from shedding a
bitter tear). No, slowly it dawned on me that neither
of Alice's Adventures were an analogy of Parkinson's.
But equally that they described me and my feelings.
Everything does get curiouser and curiouser-- and yet
I take it with equanimity, as did Alice. Fatigue is a
main factor, we all sleep very badly at night, that goes
with the condition, the rigidity wakes you after an
hour, or if you are lucky, two, then it takes a long time
to get comfortable and able to sleep again; you sit
around, move a bit, eat a bit... Not surprisingly you
pass out in the day quite frequently, and for even
shorter periods of time.

When I wrote that letter to describe to Professor Lees
how I felt about the grip of the Giant Hand, I
explained that my head can become like a colander.

All my thoughts, plans and intentions ooze or drip out of it and it becomes impossible to think in an ordinary manner.

At those times I need to have a hot line to a crossword, or be soothed by having poetry read to me. Then, with the medication, the power dribbles back into us and I can scoop up the mess from the carpet and cram it back into my colander of a brain. And so on.

This does not happen at first; they say you have that five year 'honeymoon' with the medicine. Then it begins to fall off in efficacy: sometimes doesn't bother to respond, is at least tardy, and sadly not so effective generally. I have had a very good innings as I have been on Madopar et al for twelve years. Anyhow, the point is that your day progresses very jerkily: every few hours you are up or down, on or off, flipped or unflipped. I never know when either state will occur, though some parts of the day tend to be more promising than others.

But this disjointedness people find hard to understand. You are like a reissue of two people. They come and say "Oh, are you having a bad day?" "No, more like a bad hour, with any luck. It's always thus." "Oh?" But it's hard to live on a Big Dipper: up, up so precariously, then: whoosh, down - it brings its own quota of surrealism.

Coupled with this is the problem of having a progressive disease, hard to remember this, we are so used to the process of getting better, that's what you concentrate on and the simple hope keeps you endeavouring. I find I can look through a catalogue and say "Um, I like that - might get it when I'm better." Or, more remarkably, "I might get it when I'm younger."

A small boy, a great godson, asked me the other day if I would like to play football with him? "I would love to," I said, "but, I'm so sorry, I am feeling rather old today. May I play when I am younger?" He looked at me consideringly, head on one side. "Yes," he said, "when you are about twenty." I thanked him much for that. But later he came slipping up alongside (I think he is five), "you can't actually get younger", he whispered, with the contrite look of being the bringer of bad news. Which, of course, it is.

That small boy could have been the fawn in "Through the Looking Glass". I have various candidates for the Red Queen, and the whole idea of running just to keep up with the present fits exactly. Rushing from square to square of the chessboard in hectic fashion sounds like a day in the life of someone with Parkinson's (inwardly, not outwardly). And I am nearly in love with the White Knight already. It is so endearing how he tumbles off his horse, with such accepting dignity. Because of course, falling over is a major part of our scenario, and much to be avoided for its long term effects. I haven't really hurt myself yet, probably because the house is so full of furniture and people that there is always something, or someone, to grab. And that grave and genial White Knight also proved his compatibility to me with the words, from his poem: *"And his answer trickled through my head, Like water through a sieve."*

My mother certainly had Parkinsonian symptoms when she was very, very old, inevitable, I believe, for we all get short of dopamine eventually. There was the shuffling movement, the drooping of the face which makes you look cross when you are not. To me that is one of the saddest and most irritating of little symptoms; horrid to be misinterpreted. And the slowness: "How are you these days, Mrs Flower?" people would enquire. "Well", she would reply, "it takes me half an hour to go to the loo, so life is never dull."

And, in the pantheon of PD's bizarre tribulations, there is something else I am deficient in, but it really is an example of serendipity. I have short term memory loss. Not in its usual form, my memory is fairly good, I think, but in the way I feel when I "come good" after a bout of genuine Parkinson's and no longer fully-working medication: I don't really believe that it will ever happen again! I pay lip service to it; try to get ahead of myself as much as possible; cook everything for tomorrow so I am not caught on the hop by unexpected visitors, or even expected ones, when I am not functioning. But in my heart of hearts I am sure I am all right now and it was just imagination, those bad times. They are history. Sincerely, I can recommend it. Invest in some short term memory loss.

The Big Dipper: up, up so precariously...
(page 125)

Chapter Thirteen

Envoi

"Grandma!"

"Yes, darling?"

The little four year old comes and stands beside my chair, is there a secret to be shared? She is herself a little miracle of modern medicine: born at only twenty four weeks she weighed the same as six small potatoes. I know this because that is what I used in an effort to explain how small she was, at a pound and half, to one of her cousins.

Now our precious survivor is contemplating the future.

"Grandma! One day I am going to be a Grandma and

have Parkinson's!"

She looks at me so gravely and I manage not to smile. But I think not, sweetheart, not the Parkinson's bit. It may be a little longer that the five-year-predictions continue, those that announce the expectations of the latest formula: on the market in five years' time but when that date arrives they are forgotten. No, but by the time this babe has reached my great age they will have conquered this malady, our learned and dedicated men and women: Parkinson's will be a dim and distant memory. As we will be, incidentally.

And, at the risk of appearing to be the Bad Fairy, the one everyone forgets to invite to the christening, or to the wedding party on Mount Olympus, and then wishes they hadn't, I have to add a chilling omen. There will be something else to take its place. There's plenty more where this came from.

Life on earth is a rollercoaster and always will be. But squeezing out of Pandora's casket, after Hope, came Endeavour, I think. All we can leave our children, and our grandchildren, are Hope and Endeavour.

THE END

Parkinsons
Turning into a Pumpkin
HD 2007

*I turned into a pumpkin
(page 14)*

Appendix

Just a few things I would like to recommend, somewhat eclectic, but all have helped, mollified or encouraged me. Here they are, with their addresses, to make introduction a simple matter.

With alternative/complementary medicine there is often more than one definitive address as there are various branches, so please do not think that this is a definitive list. Best try the Internet, and also the Parkinson's Disease Society which produced an excellent booklet a couple of years back: *"Complementary Therapies and Parkinson's Disease."* A copy of that would set anyone up.

ACUPUNCTURE:
It is never advisable to go to any old acupuncturist you hear of. Check that they are on the Register and can be vouched for, and are covered by insurance and suchlike. Then enjoy a lovely, unrushed appointment when you are encouraged to mention any little ailment that you may have: a number of minor afflictions can all add up to one basic problem and thus you can have them sorted out in one fell swoop. Fascinating.

British Acupuncture Council (BAcC)
63 Jeddo Road,
London,
W12 9HQ

Telephone: 020 8735 0400
www.acupuncture.org.uk

BOOKS

a. *"Understanding Parkinson's Disease"* by Dr J. M. S. Pearce

I really like this little book. For a start, it is small and slim and I like slim books, I have a dread of non-fiction books that want to be fat, and that achieve this by repeating themselves in different ways each chapter. Sadly, not unlike all too many sermons... (and perhaps one reason why I never seem to go to church).

Published in the Family Doctor Series in association with the BMA. Hope it is still around. It cost £2.49 in those early days of my own involvement, and one can always try Amazon for secondhand books.

b. *"Parkinson's at your Fingertips"* by Dr Marie Oxtoby and Professor Adrian Williams

Dauntingly big and thick, but for a good reason because everything is within, now in its Third Edition. But personally, I would like to simmer in my malady a while, before taking on something quite so comprehensive.

Published by Class Health. ISBN 1 872362 96 6

BOWEN THERAPY

The Bowen Therapists' European Register
P.O. Box 2920
Stratford-upon-Avon CV37 9ZL

Telephone: 07986 008384
Website www.bowentherapists.com

CRANIAL OSTEOPATHY

Sutherland Cranial College
P.O. Box 91
Chepstow
NP16 7ZS

Telephone: 01291 689908
Website: www.scc-osteopathy.co.uk

HEALTH FOODS
One of the postal providers of pills and potions, for instance Ginkgo biloba pills and Aloe vera cream, "Nature's Best" has always given me excellent service. Quick, reasonably priced and of seemingly high quality (how can one tell?), it is wide-ranging too. Add to this a help desk, where you can get advice and check that you are not about to take something that will disagree with your current medications.

Nature's Best
Century Place
Tunbridge Wells
Kent
TN2 3BE

Telephone: 01892 552188
Website: www.naturesbest.co.uk

HOMEOPATHY

The Society of Homeopaths
11 Brookfield
Duncan Close
Moulton Park
Northampton
N3 6WL

Telephone: 0845 450 6611
Website: www.homeopathy-soh.org

INTEGRATED HEALTH

I haven't had anything to do with this institution myself, have only just been told about it, but it sounds a splendid idea - one of Prince Charles', incidentally. In the Prince's own words, the Foundation aims for: *"more patients and doctors seeing the benefits of drawing on traditional knowledge as well as modern science to help people lead healthier lives."*

A bit difficult to find out what they actually do, but I'm sure they would be helpful if you had a problem getting the two medical disciplines together. Ours is a good case in point.

The Prince's Foundation for Integrated Health
33-41 Dallington Street
London
EC1V 0BB

Tel: 020 3119 3100
Website: www.fih.org.uk

NANDINA DOMESTICA or HEAVENLY BAMBOO
Actually not related to the bamboo at all, so that's a good start. It is probably very foolish of me to include this, and possibly it has no place in the saga of Parkinson's disease. But it is such a pretty little tree anyhow, that I feel it is worth a gamble. The story unfolds thus:

A very dear and kind friend of mine, tuning in at the end of a radio programme, was in time to hear that this little tree is supposed to keep nightmares and hallucinations at bay. Knowing my provenance she went straight out and bought me one. And there it has sat, in a tub outside the kitchen door, ever since, looking thoroughly pleased with its circumstances. It is very dainty and has flowers at the same time as berries, so there is something rather other worldly about it. And it has to be admitted that I do not have so many bad dreams as I have been wont to have, all my life. (Can talking to it sometimes, and running my fingers through its branches, account for anything like treatment?). Apparently in China and Japan the Sacred Bamboo is used to decorate temples. The people at Kew were very interested, and interesting, when I wrote to them about this. I had a long letter back telling me all sorts of historical allusions. And one of the neurologists at the National Hospital told me since that there is a doctor in America researching its possibly special powers.

I think you can buy it almost anywhere, but if your local garden centre can't help then at least we know the Royal Botanic Gardens at Kew can.

PARKINSON'S DISEASE SOCIETY

The Parkinson's Disease Society, is a must of course. And getting better and better all the time, I reckon. I wasn't very keen or impressed to begin with (three unanswered letters didn't put me in a good mood, and that was just a start) but I'd be surprised if they are not much better now. The quarterly magazine improves all the time and is now very informative, worth the modest price of a year's membership any day: big and glossy and large print, and lots of questions from those who actually have PD. £10 for a year's subscription and this will also put you in touch with your local group, should you so wish. Now at last you can talk all you like about weird symptoms without feeling a bore. There are over 330 branches and support groups. And I have been asked to tell you that there is a new handbook, with video, out called *"Keeping Moving"*—Exercise and Parkinson's. I tell this in some embarrassment because it is well known that I do no exercises. I just struggle to keep gardening, and am obviously losing because where I used to tumble forward into roses and lavender, or a clump of phlox, say, now it is mostly into a plantation of nettles.

Parkinson's Disease Society
215 Vauxhall Bridge Road
London SW1V 1EJ

Telephone 020 7931 8080
Helpline: 0808 800 0303
Textphone: (minicom) 020 7963 9380
E-mail: enquiries@parkinsons.org.uk
Website: www.parkinsons.org.uk

PATIENT VOICES
Patient Voices is a digital collection of patients' stories which can be accessed on the internet. The idea is to put patients at the heart of health care; the initiative having been supported and funded by the NHS Clinical Governance Support team. Find out more by visiting the website at: www.pilgrim.myzen.co.uk/patientvoices/

Or write to:
Patient Voices Programme
Pilgrim Projects Limited
91 Waterbeach Road
Landbeach
Cambridgeshire
CB4 8EA

Only just heard about it so cannot say more.

PILL BOX
Now this is something I cannot recommend highly enough.
Without it I would never remember to take all my pills on time,
nor be sure I was taking the right ones. I load it up every
morning with one day's supply (a whole heap of little bottles
having been thus previously primed)...

The Wonder Pill Box Timer.
Comes from:
RNB Supplies
7 Daleham Gardens
London
NW3 5BY

Telephone: 0207 435 8418/2417
E-mail: davinaben@talktalk.net

The £18 price includes post and packing. And if you are not
absolutely satisfied you can get a complete refund (within
fourteen days, that is). It is small and neat enough to fit snugly
into any pocket, and its insistent chirping calls you to a pill-
swallowing session.

REFLEXOLOGY

Association of Reflexologists (AoR)
27 Old Gloucester Street
London   WC1N 3XX
Telephone: 0870 5673320
Email: info@aor.org.uk

International Federation of Reflexologists
76-78 Edridge Road
Croydon
Surrey
CR0 1EF

Telephone: 020 8645 9134
Website: www.intfedreflexologists.org

REIKI
Amazingly, Reiki is something that can be learnt swiftly and you can even treat yourself so if you can help minimise the pain of rigidity thus could definitely a Good Thing.

The Reiki Association
2 Manor Cottages
Stockley Hill
Peterchurch
Herefordshire   HR2 0SS

Telephone: 01981 550 829

I have been given the one above but the PDS gives:

UK Reiki Federation
PO Box 1785
Andover   SP11 0WB

Telephone: 01264 773774
Email: Enquiry@reikifed.co.uk

STICK/STOOL

And the next highly recommended: my constant companion and most reliable of aids. This one actually belonged to my mother before me - and is still going strong. I call it my stick/stool, but it goes under various names. Don't be put off by there being more to it than an ordinary walking stick: the pair of feet give you much more support when walking along and you soon get into an easy rhythm with them. Then, with one insouciant flick of your thumb you can open it out and sit down in a dignified manner while you wait for the little green man, or whatever. I have sat on it for nearly an hour at one stretch, with no real discomfort.

It is available at about £40 from:

The National Trust
Heelis
Kemble Drive
Swindon
Wiltshire
SN2 2NA

Telephone: 01793 817537
Website: www.nationaltrust.org.uk

I have also seen it in a catalogue from *"The House of Bath"*. Here it is called a "Folding Event Seat" and is only £19.95. Sounds good but you probably need to have a careful look at both.

Telephone: 0871 984 2000
Website: www.houseofbath.co.uk

Parties are so much more fun when you have one of these: instead of sitting lowdown on a sofa or armchair, waiting rather pathetically for someone to come and talk to you - and even then there is that awkwardness that comes of speaking down, literally, to someone; somehow it doesn't flow. With your stick/stool, or whatever you call it, you amble up to people and join them wherever they are; you are lower but not so low. And you are not standing, most dread position of all...

GOOD LUCK!

To order copies of **'Ponderings on Parkinson's'** visit

our website www.ferryhousebooks.co.uk or ask any

bookshop to order it for you, quoting the ISBN

number (978-0-9557011-0-8).